P9-CPY-419

# A★HUNDRED★FABLES
## OF
# LA★FONTAINE

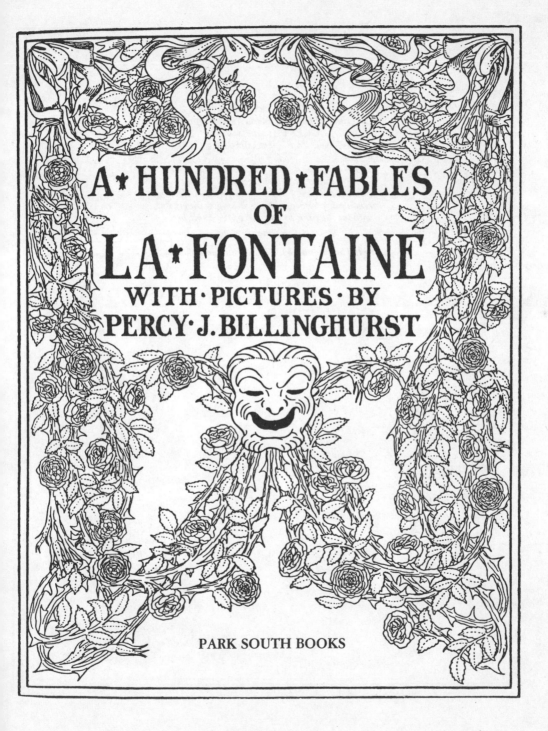

# A ★ HUNDRED ★ FABLES
## OF
# LA ★ FONTAINE
## WITH · PICTURES · BY
## PERCY · J · BILLINGHURST

PARK SOUTH BOOKS

This edition published 1988 by Park South Books
An imprint of Publishers Marketing Enterprises Inc.
386 Park Avenue South
New York, New York 10016

All rights reserved. This publication may not be
reproduced, stored in a retrieval system,
or transmitted, in any form or by any means, electronic,
mechanical, photocopying, recording or otherwise,
without the prior permission of the publishers.

ISBN 0-917923-24-3

Printed and bound by WBC, Bristol and Maesteg.

# CONTENTS.

# CONTENTS.

# A ★ HUNDRED ★ FABLES
## OF
# LA ★ FONTAINE

A GRASSHOPPER gay
　　Sang the summer away,
And found herself poor
By the winter's first roar.
Of meat or of bread,
Not a morsel she had!
So a-begging she went,
To her neighbour the ant,
　　For the loan of some wheat,
　　Which would serve her to eat,
Till the season came round.
　　"I will pay you," she saith,
　　"On an animal's faith,
Double weight in the pound
Ere the harvest be bound."
　　The ant is a friend
　　(And here she might mend)
　　Little given to lend.
"How spent you the summer?"
　　Quoth she, looking shame
　　At the borrowing dame.
"Night and day to each comer
　　I sang, if you please."
　　"You sang! I'm at ease;
For 'tis plain at a glance,
Now, ma'am, you must dance."

THE·GRASSHOPPER AND
THE·ANT.

TWO thieves, pursuing their profession,
   Had of a donkey got possession,
Whereon a strife arose,
Which went from words to blows.
The question was, to sell, or not to sell;
But while our sturdy champions fought it well,
   Another thief, who chanced to pass,
   With ready wit rode off the ass.

*This ass is, by interpretation,*
*Some province poor, or prostrate nation.*
*The thieves are princes this and that,*
*On spoils and plunder prone to fat,—*
*As those of Austria, Turkey, Hungary.*
*(Instead of two, I've quoted three—*
*Enough of such commodity.)*
*These powers engaged in war all,*
*Some fourth thief stops the quarrel,*
     *According all to one key,*
     *By riding off the donkey*

## THE·THIEVES·AND·THE·ASS.

# The Wolf Accusing the Fox.

A WOLF, affirming his belief
    That he had suffer'd by a thief,
  Brought up his neighbour fox—
Of whom it was by all confess'd,
His character was not the best—
  To fill the prisoner's box.
As judge between these vermin,
A monkey graced the ermine;
And truly other gifts of Themis
  Did scarcely seem his;
For while each party plead his cause,
Appealing boldly to the laws,
And much the question vex'd,
Our monkey sat perplex'd.
  Their words and wrath expended,
Their strife at length was ended;
When, by their malice taught,
The judge this judgment brought:
"Your characters, my friends, I long have known,
  As on this trial clearly shown;
And hence I fine you both—the grounds at large
  To state would little profit—
You wolf, in short, as bringing groundless charge,
  You fox, as guilty of it."

*Come at it right or wrong, the judge opined
No other than a villain could be fined*

6

THE·WOLF·ACCUSING·THE·FOX··
·BEFORE·THE·MONKEY···

# The Lion and the Ass Hunting.

THE king of animals, with royal grace,
　　Would celebrate his birthday in the chase.
'Twas not with bow and arrows,
To slay some wretched sparrows;
The lion hunts the wild boar of the wood,
The antlered deer and stags, the fat and good.
　　This time, the king, t' insure success,
　　Took for his aide-de-camp an ass,
　　A creature of stentorian voice,
　　That felt much honour'd by the choice.
The lion hid him in a proper station,
And order'd him to bray, for his vocation,
　　Assured that his tempestuous cry
　　The boldest beasts would terrify,
　　And cause them from their lairs to fly.
And, sooth, the horrid noise the creature made
Did strike the tenants of the wood with dread;
　　And, as they headlong fled,
All fell within the lion's ambuscade.
　　"Has not my service glorious
　　Made both of us victorious?"
　　Cried out the much-elated ass.
"Yes," said the lion; "bravely bray'd!
　　Had I not known yourself and race,
I should have been myself afraid!"
　　The donkey, had he dared,
　　With anger would have flared
At this retort, though justly made;
　　For who could suffer boasts to pass
　　So ill-befitting to an ass?

8

THE·LION·AND·THE·ASS·HUNTING.

# The Wolf turned Shepherd.

A WOLF, whose gettings from the flocks
    Began to be but few,
Bethought himself to play the fox
    In character quite new.
A shepherd's hat and coat he took,
      A cudgel for a crook,
      Nor e'en the pipe forgot:
And more to seem what he was not,
Himself upon his hat he wrote,
"I'm Willie, shepherd of these sheep."
    His person thus complete,
    His crook in upraised feet,
The impostor Willie stole upon the keep.
The real Willie, on the grass asleep,
    Slept there, indeed, profoundly,
His dog and pipe slept, also soundly;
    His drowsy sheep around lay.
    As for the greatest number,
Much bless'd the hypocrite their slumber,
And hoped to drive away the flock,
Could he the shepherd's voice but mock.
    He thought undoubtedly he could.
He tried: the tone in which he spoke,
    Loud echoing from the wood,
    The plot and slumber broke;
    Sheep, dog, and man awoke.
    The wolf, in sorry plight,
    In hampering coat bedight,
    Could neither run nor fight.

*There's always leakage of deceit*
*Which makes it never safe to cheat.*
    *Whoever is a wolf had better*
    *Keep clear of hypocritic fetter.*

**THE·WOLF·TURNED·SHEPHERD.**

# The Swan and the Cook.

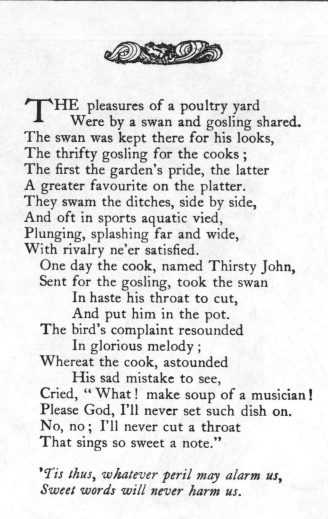

THE pleasures of a poultry yard
    Were by a swan and gosling shared.
The swan was kept there for his looks,
The thrifty gosling for the cooks ;
The first the garden's pride, the latter
A greater favourite on the platter.
They swam the ditches, side by side,
And oft in sports aquatic vied,
Plunging, splashing far and wide,
With rivalry ne'er satisfied.
    One day the cook, named Thirsty John,
    Sent for the gosling, took the swan
        In haste his throat to cut,
        And put him in the pot.
    The bird's complaint resounded
        In glorious melody ;
    Whereat the cook, astounded
        His sad mistake to see,
Cried, " What ! make soup of a musician !
Please God, I'll never set such dish on.
No, no ; I'll never cut a throat
That sings so sweet a note."

*'Tis thus, whatever peril may alarm us,*
*Sweet words will never harm us.*

## THE·SWAN·AND·THE·COOK.

# The Weasel in the Granary.

A WEASEL through a hole contrived to squeeze,
   (She was recovering from disease,)
    Which led her to a farmer's hoard.
There lodged, her wasted form she cherish'd;
   Heaven knows the lard and victuals stored
    That by her gnawing perish'd!
    Of which the consequence
    Was sudden corpulence.
    A week or so was past,
When having fully broken fast,
   A noise she heard, and hurried
To find the hole by which she came,
And seem'd to find it not the same;
   So round she ran, most sadly flurried;
And, coming back, thrust out her head,
Which, sticking there, she said,
"This is the hole, there can't be blunder:
What makes it now so small, I wonder,
Where, but the other day, I pass'd with ease?"
    A rat her trouble sees,
   And cries, "But with an emptier belly;
You enter'd lean, and lean must sally."

## THE·WEASEL·IN·THE·GRANARY

# The Shepherd and the Sea.

A SHEPHERD, neighbour to the sea,
    Lived with his flock contentedly.
His fortune, though but small,
    Was safe within his call.
At last some stranded kegs of gold
Him tempted, and his flock he sold,
Turn'd merchant, and the ocean's waves
Bore all his treasure—to its caves.
Brought back to keeping sheep once more,
But not chief shepherd, as before,
When sheep were his that grazed the shore,
He who, as Corydon or Thyrsis,
Might once have shone in pastoral verses,
Bedeck'd with rhyme and metre,
Was nothing now but Peter.
But time and toil redeem'd in full
Those harmless creatures rich in wool;
And as the lulling winds, one day,
The vessels wafted with a gentle motion,
"Want you," he cried, "more money, Madam Ocean?
Address yourself to some one else, I pray;
    You shall not get it out of me!
    I know too well your treachery."

      *This tale's no fiction, but a fact,*
      *Which, by experience back'd,*
      *Proves that a single penny,*
        *At present held, and certain,*
      *Is worth five times as many,*
        *Of Hope's, beyond the curtain;*
*That one should be content with his condition,*
*And shut his ears to counsels of ambition,*
*More faithless than the wreck-strown sea, and which*
*Doth thousands beggar where it makes one rich,—*
*Inspires the hope of wealth, in glorious forms,*
*And blasts the same with piracy and storms.*

**THE·SHEPHERD·AND·THE·SEA.**

# The Ass and the Little Dog.

ONE'S native talent from its course
    Cannot be turned aside by force;
But poorly apes the country clown
The polish'd manners of the town.
    Their Maker chooses but a few
    With power of pleasing to imbue;
    Where wisely leave it we, the mass,
    Unlike a certain fabled ass,
That thought to gain his master's blessing
By jumping on him and caressing.
    "What!" said the donkey in his heart;
    "Ought it to be that puppy's part
      To lead his useless life
        In full companionship
      With master and his wife,
        While I must bear the whip?
What doth the cur a kiss to draw?
Forsooth, he only gives his paw!
If that is all there needs to please,
I'll do the thing myself, with ease."
    Possess'd with this bright notion,—
His master sitting on his chair,
At leisure in the open air,—
    He ambled up, with awkward motion,
And put his talents to the proof;
Upraised his bruised and batter'd hoof,
And, with an amiable mien,
His master patted on the chin,
The action gracing with a word—
The fondest bray that e'er was heard!
O, such caressing was there ever?
Or melody with such a quaver?
"Ho! Martin! here! a club, a club bring!"
    Out cried the master, sore offended.
So Martin gave the ass a drubbing,—
    And so the comedy was ended.

THE·ASS·AND·THE·LITTLE·DOG

# The Man and the Wooden God.

A PAGAN kept a god of wood,—
 A sort that never hears,
 Though furnish'd well with ears,—
From which he hoped for wondrous good.
The idol cost the board of three;
 So much enrich'd was he
 With vows and offerings vain,
With bullocks garlanded and slain:
 No idol ever had, as that,
 A kitchen quite so full and fat.
But all this worship at his shrine
Brought not from this same block divine
Inheritance, or hidden mine,
 Or luck at play, or any favour.
 Nay, more, if any storm whatever
Brew'd trouble here or there,
The man was sure to have his share,
 And suffer in his purse,
Although the god fared none the worse.
At last, by sheer impatience bold,
 The man a crowbar seizes,
 His idol breaks in pieces,
And finds it richly stuff'd with gold.
"How's this?  Have I devoutly treated,"
Says he, "your godship, to be cheated?
Now leave my house, and go your way,
And search for altars where you may."

THE·MAN·AND·THE·WOODEN·GOD.

# The Ears of the Hare.

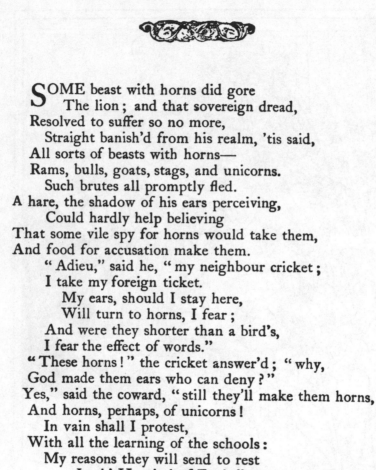

SOME beast with horns did gore
  The lion; and that sovereign dread,
Resolved to suffer so no more,
  Straight banish'd from his realm, 'tis said,
All sorts of beasts with horns—
Rams, bulls, goats, stags, and unicorns.
  Such brutes all promptly fled.
A hare, the shadow of his ears perceiving,
  Could hardly help believing
That some vile spy for horns would take them,
And food for accusation make them.
  "Adieu," said he, "my neighbour cricket;
  I take my foreign ticket.
    My ears, should I stay here,
    Will turn to horns, I fear;
  And were they shorter than a bird's,
  I fear the effect of words."
"These horns!" the cricket answer'd; "why,
God made them ears who can deny?"
Yes," said the coward, "still they'll make them horns,
And horns, perhaps, of unicorns!
  In vain shall I protest,
With all the learning of the schools:
  My reasons they will send to rest
    In th' Hospital of Fools."

**THE·EARS·OF·THE·HARE.**

# The Old Woman and Her Servants.

A BELDAM kept two spinning maids,
 Who plied so handily their trades,
Those spinning sisters down below
Were bunglers when compared with these
 No care did this old woman know
But giving tasks as she might please.
 No sooner did the god of day
  His glorious locks enkindle,
 Than both the wheels began to play,
  And from each whirling spindle
Forth danced the thread right merrily,
And back was coil'd unceasingly.
Soon as the dawn, I say, its tresses show'd,
 A graceless cock most punctual crow'd.
The beldam roused, more graceless yet,
  In greasy petticoat bedight,
  Struck up her farthing light,
And then forthwith the bed beset,
Where deeply, blessedly did snore
Those two maid-servants tired and poor.
One oped an eye, an arm one stretch'd,
And both their breath most sadly fetch'd,
This threat concealing in the sigh—
"That cursed cock shall surely die!"
And so he did:—they cut his throat,
And put to sleep his rousing note.
And yet this murder mended not
The cruel hardship of their lot;
For now the twain were scarce in bed
Before they heard the summons dread.
The beldam, full of apprehension
Lest oversleep should cause detention,
Ran like a goblin through her mansion.

*Thus often, when one thinks*  *Him in the deeper still.*
 *To clear himself from ill,* *The beldam acting for the cock,*
*His effort only sinks*  *Was Scylla for Charybdis' rock*

THE·OLD·WOMAN·
AND·HER·TWO·
SERVANTS.

# The Ass Carrying Relics.

A N ass, with relics for his load,
    Supposed the worship on the road
Meant for himself alone,
    And took on lofty airs,
Receiving as his own
    The incense and the prayers.
Some one, who saw his great mistake,
Cried, " Master Donkey, do not make
    Yourself so big a fool.
Not you they worship, but your pack ;
They praise the idols on your back,
    And count yourself a paltry tool."

*'Tis thus a brainless magistrate
Is honour'd for his robe of state.*

**THE·ASS·CARRYING·RELICS.**

# The Hare and the Partridge.

A FIELD in common share
  A partridge and a hare,
And live in peaceful state,
Till, woeful to relate !
The hunters' mingled cry
Compels the hare to fly.
He hurries to his fort,
And spoils almost the sport
By faulting every hound
That yelps upon the ground.
At last his reeking heat
Betrays his snug retreat.
Old Tray, with philosophic nose,
Snuffs carefully, and grows
  So certain, that he cries,
      "The hare is here; bow wow!"
      And veteran Ranger now,—
The dog that never lies,—
"The hare is gone," replies.
Alas! poor, wretched hare,
Back comes he to his lair,
To meet destruction there !
The partridge, void of fear,
Begins her friend to jeer :—
"You bragg'd of being fleet;
How serve you, now, your feet?"
Scarce has she ceased to speak,—
The laugh yet in her beak,—
When comes her turn to die,
From which she could not fly.
She thought her wings, indeed,
Enough for every need ;
But in her laugh and talk,
Forgot the cruel hawk !

**THE·HARE·and·THE·PARTRIDGE.**

# The Lion Going to War.

THE lion had an enterprise in hand;
    Held a war-council, sent his provost-marshal,
And gave the animals a call impartial—
Each, in his way, to serve his high command.
The elephant should carry on his back
The tools of war, the mighty public pack,
And fight in elephantine way and form;
The bear should hold himself prepared to storm;
The fox all secret stratagems should fix;
The monkey should amuse the foe by tricks.
"Dismiss," said one, "the blockhead asses,
    And hares, too cowardly and fleet."
"No," said the king; "I use all classes;
    Without their aid my force were incomplete.
The ass shall be our trumpeter, to scare
Our enemy.   And then the nimble hare
Our royal bulletins shall homeward bear."

*A monarch provident and wise*
*Will hold his subjects all of consequence,*
    *And know in each what talent lies.*
*There's nothing useless to a man of sense*

THE·LION·GOING·TO·WAR··

# The Old Man and the Ass.

AN old man, riding on his ass,
    Had found a spot of thrifty grass,
And there turn'd loose his weary beast.
Old Grizzle, pleased with such a feast,
Flung up his heels, and caper'd round,
Then roll'd and rubb'd upon the ground,
And frisk'd and browsed and bray'd,
And many a clean spot made.
Arm'd men came on them as he fed:
"Let's fly," in haste the old man said.
"And wherefore so?" the ass replied;
"With heavier burdens will they ride?"
    "No," said the man, already started.
    "Then," cried the ass, as he departed
    "I'll stay, and be—no matter whose;
Save you yourself, and leave me loose
But let me tell you, ere you go,
(I speak plain English, as you know,)
My master is my only foe."

THE·OLD·MAN·AND·THE·ASS.

# The Ass and his Masters.

A GARDENER'S ass complain'd to Destiny
    Of being made to rise before the dawn.
"The cocks their matins have not sung," said he,
    "Ere I am up and gone.
And all for what?   To market herbs, it seems.
Fine cause, indeed, to interrupt my dreams!"
    Fate, moved by such a prayer,
    Sent him a currier's load to bear,
Whose hides so heavy and ill-scented were,
    They almost choked the foolish beast.
"I wish me with my former lord," he said:
"For then, whene'er he turn'd his head,
    If on the watch, I caught
    A cabbage-leaf, which cost me nought.
But, in this horrid place, I find
No chance or windfall of the kind;—
    Or if, indeed, I do,
    The cruel blows I rue."
    Anon it came to pass
    He was a collier's ass.
Still more complaint.   "What now?" said Fate,
    Quite out of patience.
    "If on this jackass I must wait,
What will become of kings and nations?
Has none but he aught here to tease him?
Have I no business but to please him?"
    And Fate had cause;—for all are so
    Unsatisfied while here below.
Our present lot is aye the worst.
    Our foolish prayers the skies infest.
    Were Jove to grant all we request,
The din renew'd, his head would burst.

THE·ASS·AND·HIS·MASTERS···

# The Wax-Candle.

FROM bowers of gods the bees came down to man.
On Mount Hymettus, first, they say,
They made their home, and stored away
The treasures which the zephyrs fan.
When men had robb'd these daughters of the sky,
And left their palaces of nectar dry,—
Or, in English as the thing's explain'd,
When hives were of their honey drain'd—
The spoilers 'gan the wax to handle,
And fashion'd from it many a candle.
Of these, one, seeing clay, made brick by fire,
Remain uninjured by the teeth of time,
Was kindled into great desire
For immortality sublime.
And so this new Empedocles
Upon the blazing pile one sees,
Self-doom'd by purest folly
To fate so melancholy.
The candle lack'd philosophy:
All things are made diverse to be.
To wander from our destined tracks—
There cannot be a vainer wish;
But this Empedocles of wax,
That melted in chafing-dish
Was truly not a greater fool
Than he of whom we read at school.

THE·WAX~
CANDLE·

# The Shepherd and his Flock.

"WHAT! shall I lose them one by one,
　　This stupid coward throng?
And never shall the wolf have done?
　　They were at least a thousand strong,
But still they've let poor Robin fall a prey!
　　Ah, woe's the day!
　　Poor Robin Wether lying dead!
　　He follow'd for a bit of bread
His master through the crowded city,
　　And would have follow'd, had he led,
Around the world.　Oh! what a pity!
　　My pipe, and even step, he knew;
　　To meet me when I came, he flew;
In hedge-row shade we napp'd together;
　　Alas, alas, my Robin Wether!"
When Willy thus had duly said
His eulogy upon the dead,
And unto everlasting fame
Consign'd poor Robin Wether's name,
He then harangued the flock at large,
　　From proud old chieftain rams
　　Down to the smallest lambs,
Addressing them this weighty charge,—
Against the wolf, as one, to stand,
In firm, united, fearless band,
By which they might expel him from their land.
　　Upon their faith, they would not flinch,
　　They promised him, a single inch.
"We'll choke," said they, "the murderous glutton
Who robb'd us of our Robin Mutton."
　　Their lives they pledged against the beast,
　　And Willy gave them all a feast.
But evil Fate, than Phœbus faster,
Ere night had brought a new disaster:
A wolf there came.　By nature's law,
　　The total flock were prompt to run;
And yet 'twas not the wolf they saw,
But shadow of him from the setting sun.

*Harangue a craven soldiery,　　　　　Adieu to all their boast and mettle:*
*What heroes they will seem to be!　　Your own example will be vain,*
*But let them snuff the smoke of battle,　And exhortations, to retain*
*Or even hear the ramrods rattle,　　　　The timid cattle.*

THE·SHEPHERD·AND·HIS·FLOCK·

# The Tortoise and the Two Ducks.

A LIGHT-BRAIN'D tortoise, anciently,
　　Tired of her hole, the world would see.
Prone are all such, self-banish'd, to roam—
Prone are all cripples to abhor their home.
　Two ducks, to whom the gossip told
　The secret of her purpose bold,
　　Profess'd to have the means whereby
　　They could her wishes gratify.
"Our boundless road," said they, "behold!
　　　It is the open air;
　　　And through it we will bear
　　You safe o'er land and ocean.
　Republics, kingdoms, you will view,
　And famous cities, old and new;
　　　And get of customs, laws, a notion,—
Of various wisdom various pieces,
As did, indeed, the sage Ulysses."
　The eager tortoise waited not
　To question what Ulysses got,
　But closed the bargain on the spot.
　A nice machine the birds devise
　To bear their pilgrim through the skies.
　Athwart her mouth a stick they throw:
　"Now bite it hard, and don't let go,"
　They say, and seize each duck an end,
　And, swiftly flying, upward tend.
　It made the people gape and stare
　　Beyond the expressive power of words,
　To see a tortoise cut the air,
　　Exactly poised between two birds.
"A miracle," they cried, "is seen!
There goes the flying tortoise queen!"
"The queen!" ('twas thus the tortoise spoke;)
"I'm truly that, without a joke."
Much better had she held her tongue,
For, opening that whereby she clung,
Before the gazing crowd she fell,
And dash'd to bits her brittle shell.

*Imprudence, vanity, and babble,*　　*An ever-undivided rabble,*
　*And idle curiosity,*　　　　　*Have all the same paternity.*

THE·TORTOISE·AND·THE·TWO·DUCKS·

# The Two Asses.

TWO asses tracking, t'other day,
   Of which each in his turn,
Did incense to the other burn,
   Quite in the usual way,—
I heard one to his comrade say,
   "My lord, do you not find
The prince of knaves and fools
To be this man, who boasts of mind
   Instructed in his schools?
With wit unseemly and profane,
   He mocks our venerable race—
On each of his who lacketh brain
   Bestows our ancient surname, ass!
And, with abusive tongue portraying,
Describes our laugh and talk as braying!
These bipeds of their folly tell us,
While thus pretending to excel us."
"No, 'tis for you to speak, my friend,
   And let their orators attend.
The braying is their own, but let them be:
We understand each other, and agree,
   And that's enough.   As for your song,
Such wonders to its notes belong,
The nightingale is put to shame,
The Sirens lose one half their fame."
"My lord," the other ass replied,
"Such talents in yourself reside,
Of asses all, the joy and pride."
These donkeys, not quite satisfied
With scratching thus each other's hide,
   Must needs the cities visit,
   Their fortunes there to raise,
   By sounding forth the praise,
Each, of the other's skill exquisite.

## THE·TWO·ASSES.

# The Shepherd and his Dog.

A SHEPHERD, with a single dog,
　　Was ask'd the reason why
He kept a dog, whose least supply
Amounted to a loaf of bread
For every day.　The people said
He'd better give the animal
To guard the village seignior's hall;
For him, a shepherd, it would be
A thriftier economy
To keep small curs, say two or three,
That would not cost him half the food,
And yet for watching be as good.
The fools, perhaps, forgot to tell
If they would fight the wolf as well.
The silly shepherd, giving heed,
Cast off his dog of mastiff breed,
And took three dogs to watch his cattle,
Which ate far less, but fled in battle.

*Not vain our tale, if it convinces*
　　*Small states that 'tis a wiser thing*
　　*To trust a single powerful king,*
*Than half a dozen petty princes.*

THE·SHEPHERD·AND·HIS·DOG···

# The Two Mules.

TWO mules were bearing on their backs,
　　One, oats ; the other, silver of the tax.
The latter glorying in his load,
　March'd proudly forward on the road ;
And, from the jingle of his bell,
'Twas plain he liked his burden well.
　　But in a wild-wood glen
　　A band of robber men
Rush'd forth upon the twain.
　　Well with the silver pleased,
　　They by the bridle seized
The treasure mule so vain.
Poor mule ! in struggling to repel
His ruthless foes, he fell
Stabb'd through ; and with a bitter sighing,
　He cried, "Is this the lot they promised me ?
My humble friend from danger free,
While, weltering in my gore, I'm dying ? "
　　"My friend," his fellow-mule replied,
" It is not well to have one's work too high.
If thou hadst been a miller's drudge, as I,
　Thou wouldst not thus have died."

**THE·TWO·MULES.**

# The Heifer, the Goat, and the Sheep.

THE heifer, the goat, and their sister the sheep,
    Compacted their earnings in common to keep,
'Tis said, in time past, with a lion, who sway'd
Full lordship o'er neighbours, of whatever grade.
The goat, as it happen'd, a stag having snared,
Sent off to the rest, that the beast might be shared.
All gather'd; the lion first counts on his claws,
And says, "We'll proceed to divide with our paws
The stag into pieces, as fix'd by our laws."
    This done, he announces part first as his own;
    "'Tis mine," he says, "truly, as lion alone."
    To such a decision there's nought to be said,
    As he who has made it is doubtless the head.
"Well, also, the second to me should belong;
'Tis mine, be it known, by the right of the strong.
Again, as the bravest, the third must be mine.
To touch but the fourth whoso maketh a sign,
            I'll choke him to death
            In the space of a breath!"

THE·HEIFER, THE GOAT, & THE SHEEP.

# The Two Rats, the Fox, and the Egg.

TWO rats in foraging fell on an egg,—
    For gentry such as they
A genteel dinner every way;
They needed not to find an ox's leg.
    Brimful of joy and appetite,
      They were about to sack the box,
      So tight without the aid of locks,
When suddenly there came in sight
    A personage—Sir Pullet Fox.
Sure, luck was never more untoward
Since Fortune was a vixen froward!
How should they save their egg—and bacon?
    Their plunder couldn't then be bagg'd;
Should it in forward paws be taken,
    Or roll'd along, or dragg'd?
    Each method seem'd impossible,
    And each was then of danger full.
Necessity, ingenious mother,
Brought forth what help'd them from their pother.
As still there was a chance to save their prey,—
The sponger yet some hundred yards away,—
One seized the egg, and turn'd upon his back,
And then, in spite of many a thump and thwack,
That would have torn, perhaps, a coat of mail,
    The other dragg'd him by the tail.
    Who dares the inference to blink,
    That beasts possess wherewith to think?

*Were I commission'd to bestow*
*This power on creatures here below,*
*The beasts should have as much of mind*
*As infants of the human kind.*

THE·TWO·RATS·THE·FOX·AND·THE·EGG.

# The Man and his Image.

A MAN, who had no rivals in the love
   Which to himself he bore,
Esteem'd his own dear beauty far above
   What earth had seen before.
More than contented in his error,
He lived the foe of every mirror.
Officious fate, resolved our lover
From such an illness should recover,
Presented always to his eyes
The mute advisers which the ladies prize;—
Mirrors in parlours, inns, and shops,—
Mirrors the pocket furniture of fops,—
Mirrors on every lady's zone,
From which his face reflected shone.
What could our dear Narcissus do?
From haunts of men he now withdrew,
On purpose that his precious shape
From every mirror might escape.
   But in his forest glen alone,
     Apart from human trace,
     A watercourse,
     Of purest source,
While with unconscious gaze
He pierced its waveless face,
   Reflected back his own.
Incensed with mingled rage and fright,
He seeks to shun the odious sight;
But yet that mirror sheet, so clear and still,
He cannot leave, do what he will.

*Ere this, my story's drift you plainly see.*
*From such mistake there is no mortal free.*
   *That obstinate self-lover*
   *The human soul doth cover;*
*The mirrors follies are of others,*
*In which, as all are genuine brothers,*
*Each soul may see to life depicted*
*Itself with just such faults afflicted;*
*And by that charming placid brook,*
*Needless to say, I mean your Maxim Book.*

THE-MAN-AND-HIS-IMAGE

# The Dragon with Many Heads.

$\mathbf{A}^{N}$ envoy of the Porte Sublime,
    As history says, once on a time,
Before th' imperial German court
Did rather boastfully report,
The troops commanded by his master's firman,
As being a stronger army than the German:
    To which replied a Dutch attendant,
    "Our prince has more than one dependant
Who keeps an army at his own expense."
    The Turk, a man of sense,
    Rejoin'd, "I am aware
What power your emperor's servants share.
It brings to mind a tale both strange and true,
A thing which once, myself, I chanced to view.
    I saw come darting through a hedge,
    Which fortified a rocky ledge,
    A hydra's hundred heads; and in a trice
    My blood was turning into ice.
    But less the harm than terror,—
    The body came no nearer;
    Nor could, unless it had been sunder'd,
    To parts at least a hundred.
    While musing deeply on this sight,
    Another dragon came to light,
    Whose single head avails
    To lead a hundred tails:
And, seized with juster fright,
    I saw him pass the hedge,—
    Head, body, tails,—a wedge
Of living and resistless powers.—
The other was your emperor's force; this ours."

**THE·DRAGON·WITH·MANY·HEADS·**

# Death and the Woodman.

A POOR wood-chopper, with his fagot load,
    Whom weight of years, as well as load, oppress'd,
Sore groaning in his smoky hut to rest,
Trudged wearily along his homeward road.
At last his wood upon the ground he throws,
And sits him down to think o'er all his woes.
To joy a stranger, since his hapless birth,
What poorer wretch upon this rolling earth?
No bread sometimes, and ne'er a moment's rest;
Wife, children, soldiers, landlords, public tax,
All wait the swinging of his old, worn axe,
And paint the veriest picture of a man unblest.
On Death he calls.  Forthwith that monarch grim
Appears, and asks what he should do for him.
"Not much, indeed; a little help I lack—
To put these fagots on my back."

> *Death ready stands all ills to cure;*
>    *But let us not his cure invite.*
> *Than die, 'tis better to endure,—*
>    *Is both a manly maxim and a right.*

## DEATH·AND·THE·WOODMAN.

"THE artist by his work is known."
    A piece of honey-comb, one day,
Discover'd as a waif and stray,
The hornets treated as their own.
Their title did the bees dispute,
And brought before a wasp the suit.
The judge was puzzled to decide,
For nothing could be testified
Save that around this honey-comb
There had been seen, as if at home,
Some longish, brownish, buzzing creatures,
Much like the bees in wings and features.
But what of that? for marks the same,
The hornets, too, could truly claim.
Between assertion, and denial,
The wasp, in doubt, proclaim'd new trial;
And, hearing what an ant-hill swore,
Could see no clearer than before.
"What use, I pray, of this expense?"
At last exclaim'd a bee of sense.
    "We've labour'd months in this affair,
    And now are only where we were.
        Meanwhile the honey runs to waste:
'Tis time the judge should show some haste.
The parties, sure, have had sufficient bleeding,
Without more fuss of scrawls and pleading.
Let's set ourselves at work, these drones and we
And then all eyes the truth may plainly see,
    Whose art it is that can produce
    The magic cells, the nectar juice."
        The hornets, flinching on their part,
        Show that the work transcends their art.
        The wasp at length their title sees,
        And gives the honey to the bees.

        *Would God that suits at law with us*
        *Might all be managed thus!*

**THE·HORNETS·AND·THE·BEES**

# The Oak and the Reed.

THE oak one day address'd the reed:—
 "To you ungenerous indeed
Has nature been, my humble friend,
With weakness aye obliged to bend.
The smallest bird that flits in air
Is quite too much for you to bear;
The slightest wind that wreathes the lake
Your ever-trembling head doth shake.
The while, my towering form | Dares with the mountain top
The solar blaze to stop, | And wrestle with the storm.
What seems to you the blast of death,
To me is but a zephyr's breath.
Beneath my branches had you grown,
Less suffering would your life have known,
Unhappily you oftenest show
 In open air your slender form,
Along the marshes wet and low,
 That fringe the kingdom of the storm.
 To you, declare I must,
 Dame Nature seems unjust."
Then modestly replied the reed:
"Your pity, sir, is kind indeed,
But wholly needless for my sake.
The wildest wind that ever blew
Is safe to me compared with you.
I bend, indeed, but never break.
Thus far, I own, the hurricane
Has beat your sturdy back in vain;
But wait the end."  Just at the word,
The tempest's hollow voice was heard.
The North sent forth her fiercest child,
Dark, jagged, pitiless, and wild.
The oak, erect, endured the blow;
The reed bow'd gracefully and low.
But, gathering up its strength once more,
In greater fury than before,
The savage blast | O'erthrew, at last,
That proud, old, sky-encircled head,
Whose feet entwined the empire of the dead!

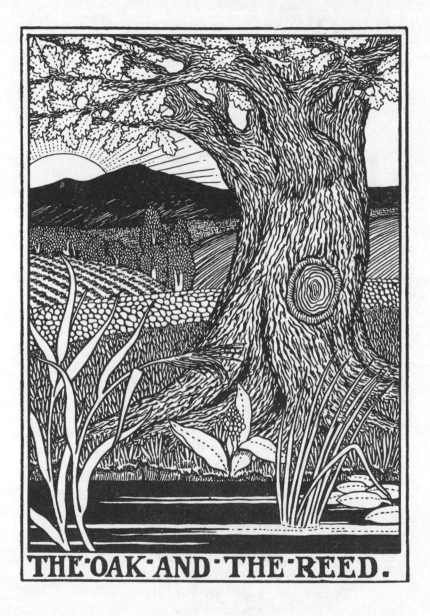

THE·OAK·AND·THE·REED.

OLD Rodilard, a certain cat,
　　Such havoc of the rats had made,
'Twas difficult to find a rat
　　With nature's debt unpaid.
The few that did remain,
　　To leave their holes afraid,
From usual food abstain,
　　Not eating half their fill.
　　And wonder no one will
That one who made of rats his revel,
With rats pass'd not for cat, but devil.
Now, on a day, this dread rat-eater,
Who had a wife, went out to meet her;
And while he held his caterwauling,
The unkill'd rats, their chapter calling,
Discuss'd the point, in grave debate,
How they might shun impending fate.
　　Their dean, a prudent rat,
Thought best, and better soon than late,
　　To bell the fatal cat;
That, when he took his hunting round,
The rats, well caution'd by the sound,
Might hide in safety under ground;
　　Indeed he knew no other means.
And all the rest | At once confess'd
　　Their minds were with the dean's.
No better plan, they all believed,
Could possibly have been conceived.
No doubt the thing would work right well,
If any one would hang the bell.
　　But, one by one, said every rat,
　　"I'm not so big a fool as that."
The plan knock'd up in this respect,
The council closed without effect.

And many a council I have seen,
Or reverend chapter with its dean,
　　That, thus resolving wisely,
　　Fell through like this precisely.

*To argue or refute*　　　　　　*The man to execute*
　*Wise counselors abound;*　　　*Is harder to be found.*

## THE·COUNCIL·HELD·BY·THE·RATS.

# The Two Bulls and the Frog.

TWO bulls engaged in shocking battle,
  Both for a certain heifer's sake,
And lordship over certain cattle,
  A frog began to groan and quake.
    "But what is this to you?"
Inquired another of the croaking crew.
    "Why, sister, don't you see,
    The end of this will be,
That one of these big brutes will yield,
And then be exiled from the field?
No more permitted on the grass to feed,
He'll forage through our marsh, on rush and reed;
    And while he eats or chews the cud,
    Will trample on us in the mud.
    Alas! to think how frogs must suffer
    By means of this proud lady heifer!"
This fear was not without good sense.
One bull was beat, and much to their expense;
For, quick retreating to their reedy bower,
He trod on twenty of them in an hour.

  *Of little folks it oft has been the fate*
  *To suffer for the follies of the great.*

## THE·TWO·BULLS·AND·THE·FROG.

# The Bat and the Two Weasels.

A BLUNDERING bat once stuck her head
　　Into a wakeful weasel's bed;
Whereat the mistress of the house,
　　A deadly foe of rats and mice,
　　Was making ready in a trice
To eat the stranger as a mouse.
　　"What! do you dare," she said, "to creep in
The very bed I sometimes sleep in,
Now, after all the provocation
I've suffered from your thievish nation?
Are you not really a mouse,
That gnawing pest of every house,
Your special aim to do the cheese ill?
Ay, that you are, or I'm no weasel."
　　"I beg your pardon," said the bat;
"My kind is very far from that.
What! I a mouse! Who told you such a lie?
Why, ma'am, I am a bird; | And, if you doubt my word,
　　Just see the wings with which I fly.
　　Long live the mice that cleave the sky!"
　　　　These reasons had so fair a show,
　　　　The weasel let the creature go.

By some strange fancy led, | The same wise blunderhead,
　　　　But two or three days later,
Had chosen for her rest | Another weasel's nest,
　　This last, of birds a special hater.
　　　　New peril brought this step absurd:
　　Without a moment's thought or puzzle,
　　Dame weasel opened her peaked muzzle
　　　　To eat th' intruder as a bird.
　　"Hold! do not wrong me," cried the bat;
　　"I'm truly no such thing as that.
Your eyesight strange conclusions gathers.
What makes a bird, I pray? Its feathers.
　　I'm cousin of the mice and rats.
　　Great Jupiter confound the cats!"
　　The bat, by such adroit replying,
　　Twice saved herself from dying.

*And many a human stranger*　　*And sings, as suits, where'er he goes,*
*Thus turns his coat in danger;*　　*"God save the king!"—or "save his foes!"*

66

THE·BAT·AND·THE·TWO·WEASELS.

# The Bird wounded by an Arrow.

A BIRD, with plumèd arrow shot,
     In dying case deplored her lot :
" Alas ! " she cried, " the anguish of the thought !
This ruin partly by myself was brought !
     Hard-hearted men ! from us to borrow
     What wings to us the fatal arrow !
     But mock us not, ye cruel race,
     For you must often take our place."

*The work of half the human brothers*
*Is making arms against the others.*

THE·
BIRD·
WOUNDED·
BY·AN·
ARROW.

# The Lion and the Gnat.

" GO, paltry insect, nature's meanest brat!"
          Thus said the royal lion to the gnat.
The gnat declared immediate war.
   "Think you," said he, " your royal name
          To me worth caring for?
Think you I tremble at your power or fame?
   The ox is bigger far than you;
   Yet him I drive, and all his crew."
This said, as one that did no fear owe,
   Himself he blew the battle charge,
   Himself both trumpeter and hero.
   At first he play'd about at large,
Then on the lion's neck, at leisure, settled,
And there the royal beast full sorely nettled.
   With foaming mouth, and flashing eye,
   He roars.   All creatures hide or fly,—
          Such mortal terror at
          The work of one poor gnat!
With constant change of his attack,
The snout now stinging, now the back,
And now the chambers of the nose;
The pigmy fly no mercy shows.
   The lion's rage was at its height;
   His viewless foe now laugh'd outright,
   When on his battle-ground he saw,
   That every savage tooth and claw
          Had got its proper beauty
          By doing bloody duty;
Himself, the hapless lion, tore his hide,
And lash'd with sounding tail from side to side.
   Ah! bootless blow, and bite, and curse!
   He beat the harmless air, and worse;
          For, though so fierce and stout,
          By effort wearied out,
   He fainted, fell, gave up the quarrel;
   The gnat retires with verdant laurel.

*We often have the most to fear    Again, great risks a man may clear,*
   *From those we most despise;    Who by the smallest dies.*

THE·LION·AND·THE·GNAT··

# The Ass Loaded with Sponges.

A MAN, whom I shall call an ass-eteer,
　　His sceptre like some Roman emperor bearing,
Drove on two coursers of protracted ear,
The one, with sponges laden, briskly faring;
　　　　The other lifting legs
　　　　As if he trod on eggs,
　　　With constant need of goading,
　　　And bags of salt for loading.
O'er hill and dale our merry pilgrims pass'd,
Till, coming to a river's ford at last,
They stopp'd quite puzzled on the shore.
Our asseteer had cross'd the stream before;
　　So, on the lighter beast astride,
　　　He drives the other, spite of dread,
　　　Which, loath indeed to go ahead,
　　Into a deep hole turns aside,
　　　　And, facing right about,
　　　　Where he went in, comes out;
　　　For duckings, two or three
　　　　Had power the salt to melt,
　　　　So that the creature felt
　　　His burden'd shoulders free.
　　The sponger, like a sequent sheep,
　　Pursuing through the water deep,
　　　　Into the same hole plunges
　　　Himself, his rider, and the sponges.
All three drank deeply: asseteer and ass
For boon companions of their load might pass;
　　Which last became so sore a weight,
　　　The ass fell down, | Belike to drown
　　　His rider risking equal fate.
　　A helper came, no matter who.

　　*The moral needs no more ado—*
　　　*That all can't act alike,—*
　　　*The point I wish'd to strike.*

**THE·ASS·LOADED·WITH·SPONGES.**

# The Dove and the Ant.

A DOVE came to a brook to drink,
   When, leaning o'er its crumbling brink,
An ant fell in, and vainly tried,
In this, to her, an ocean tide,
To reach the land; whereat the dove,
With every living thing in love,
Was prompt a spire of grass to throw her,
By which the ant regain'd the shore.

A barefoot scamp, both mean and sly,
Soon after chanced this dove to spy;
And, being arm'd with bow and arrow,
   The hungry codger doubted not
   The bird of Venus, in his pot,
Would make a soup before the morrow.
   Just as his deadly bow he drew,
      Our ant just bit his heel.
      Roused by the villain's squeal,
   The dove took timely hint, and flew
      Far from the rascal's coop;—
      And with her flew his soup

THE·
DOVE·
AND·
THE·
ANT.

# The Cock and the Fox.

UPON a tree there mounted guard
    A veteran cock, adroit and cunning;
When to the roots a fox up running,
Spoke thus, in tones of kind regard :—
    "Our quarrel, brother, 's at an end;
    Henceforth I hope to live your friend;
        For peace now reigns
    Throughout the animal domains.
I bear the news :—come down, I pray,
    And give me the embrace fraternal;
And please, my brother, don't delay.
    So much the tidings do concern all,
That I must spread them far to-day.
Now you and yours can take your walks
Without a fear or thought of hawks.
And should you clash with them or others,
In us you'll find the best of brothers;—
For which you may, this joyful night,
    Your merry bonfires light.
        But, first, let's seal the bliss
    With one fraternal kiss."
"Good friend," the cock replied, "upon my word,
A better thing I never heard;
        And doubly I rejoice
        To hear it from your voice;
And, really there must be something in it,
For yonder come two greyhounds, which I flatter
Myself are couriers on this very matter.
    They come so fast, they'll be here in a minute.
I'll down, and all of us will seal the blessing
    With general kissing and caressing."
    "Adieu," said fox; "my errand's pressing;
        I'll hurry on my way,
        And we'll rejoice some other day."
So off the fellow scamper'd, quick and light,
To gain the fox-holes of a neighbouring height,
Less happy in his stratagem than flight.
    The cock laugh'd sweetly in his sleeve;—
    'Tis doubly sweet deceiver to deceive.

**THE·COCK·AND·THE·FOX·**

# The Lion beaten by the Man.

A PICTURE once was shown,
In which one man, alone,
Upon the ground had thrown
A lion fully grown.
Much gloried at the sight the rabble.
A lion thus rebuked their babble :—
"That you have got the victory there,
There is no contradiction.
But, gentles, possibly you are
The dupes of easy fiction :
Had we the art of making pictures,
Perhaps our champion had beat yours!"

THE·LION·BEATEN·BY·THE·MAN.

# Philomel and Progne.

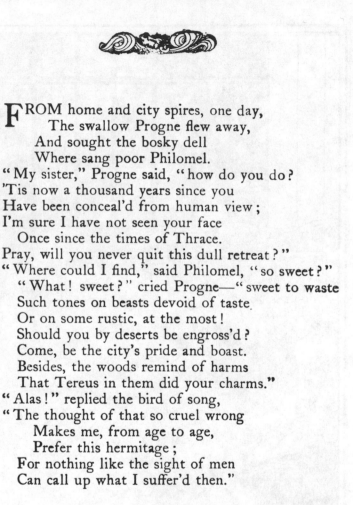

FROM home and city spires, one day,
　　The swallow Progne flew away,
　　And sought the bosky dell
　　Where sang poor Philomel.
"My sister," Progne said, "how do you do?
'Tis now a thousand years since you
Have been conceal'd from human view;
I'm sure I have not seen your face
　　Once since the times of Thrace.
Pray, will you never quit this dull retreat?"
"Where could I find," said Philomel, "so sweet?"
　　"What! sweet?" cried Progne—"sweet to waste
　　Such tones on beasts devoid of taste.
　　Or on some rustic, at the most!
　　Should you by deserts be engross'd?
　　Come, be the city's pride and boast.
　　Besides, the woods remind of harms
　　That Tereus in them did your charms."
"Alas!" replied the bird of song,
"The thought of that so cruel wrong
　　Makes me, from age to age,
　　Prefer this hermitage;
　　For nothing like the sight of men
　　Can call up what I suffer'd then."

**PHILOMEL · AND · PROGNE.**

# The Camel and the Floating Sticks.

THE first who saw the humpback'd camel
    Fled off for life; the next approach'd with care;
The third with tyrant rope did boldly dare
The desert wanderer to trammel.
    Such is the power of use to change
    The face of objects new and strange;
    Which grow, by looking at, so tame,
    They do not even seem the same.
And since this theme is up for our attention,
    A certain watchman I will mention,
      Who, seeing something far
        Away upon the ocean,
        Could not but speak his notion
      That 'twas a ship of war.
Some minutes more had past,—
    A bomb-ketch 'twas without a sail,
    And then a boat, and then a bale,
And floating sticks of wood at last!

    *Full many things on earth, I wot,*
*Will claim this tale,—and well they may;*
*They're something dreadful far away,*
    *But near at hand—they're not.*

**THE·CAMEL·AND·THE·FLOATING·STICKS**

# The Wolf, the Goat, and the Kid.

AS went a goat of grass to take her fill,
   And browse the herbage of a distant hill,
She latch'd her door, and bid,
With matron care, her kid;
" My daughter, as you live,
   This portal don't undo
   To any creature who
This watchword does not give :
' Deuce take the wolf and all his race ! ' "
The wolf was passing near the place
By chance, and heard the words with pleasure,
   And laid them up as useful treasure ;
And hardly need we mention,
Escaped the goat's attention.
   No sooner did he see
   The matron off, than he,
With hypocritic tone and face,
Cried out before the place,
" Deuce take the wolf and all his race ! "
   Not doubting thus to gain admission.
   The kid, not void of all suspicion,
   Peer'd through a crack, and cried,
      " Show me white paw before
      You ask me to undo the door."
The wolf could not, if he had died,
   For wolves have no connection
   With pains of that complexion.
So, much surprised, our gourmandiser
Retired to fast till he was wiser.

*How would the kid have been undone*
   *Had she but trusted to the word ?*
   *The wolf by chance had overheard !*
*Two sureties better are than one ;*
   *And caution's worth its cost,*
   *Though sometimes seeming lost.*

84

THE·WOLF, THE GOAT, AND THE KID

# The Rat Retired from the World.

THE sage Levantines have a tale
  About a rat that weary grew
Of all the cares which life assail,
  And to a Holland cheese withdrew.
His solitude was there profound,
Extending through his world so round.
Our hermit lived on that within;
And soon his industry had been
With claws and teeth so good,
  That in his novel hermitage,
  He had in store, for wants of age,
Both house and livelihood.
One day this personage devout,
Whose kindness none might doubt,
Was ask'd, by certain delegates
That came from Rat-United-States,
For some small aid, for they
To foreign parts were on their way,
For succour in the great cat-war.
Ratopolis beleaguer'd sore,
  Their whole republic drain'd and poor,
No morsel in their scrips they bore.
  Slight boon they craved, of succour sure
In days at utmost three or four.
"My friends," the hermit said,
"To worldly things I'm dead.
How can a poor recluse
To such a mission be of use?
What can he do but pray
That God will aid it on its way?
And so, my friends, it is my prayer
That God will have you in his care."
His well-fed saintship said no more,
But in their faces shut the door.

*What think you, reader, is the service*
  *For which I use this niggard rat?*
*To paint a monk?  No, but a dervise.*
  *A monk, I think, however fat,*
  *Must be more bountiful than that.*

THE·RAT·RETIRED·FROM·THE·WORLD.

# The Cunning Fox.

A FOX once practised, 'tis believed,
   A stratagem right well conceived.
The wretch, when in the utmost strait
By dogs of nose so delicate,
Approach'd a gallows, where,
A lesson to like passengers,
Or clothed in feathers or in furs,
Some badgers, owls, and foxes, pendent were.
Their comrade, in his pressing need,
Arranged himself among the dead.
I seem to see old Hannibal
Outwit some Roman general,
And sit securely in his tent,
The legions on some other scent.
But certain dogs, kept back
To tell the errors of the pack,
Arriving where the traitor hung,
A fault in fullest chorus sung.
Though by their bark the welkin rung,
Their master made them hold the tongue.
Suspecting not a trick so odd,
Said he, "The rogue 's beneath the sod.
My dogs, that never saw such jokes,
Won't bark beyond these honest folks."

The rogue would try the trick again.
He did so to his cost and pain.
Again with dogs the welkin rings;
Again our fox from gallows swings;
But though he hangs with greater faith
This time, he does it to his death.

   *So uniformly is it true,*
   *A stratagem is best when new.*

THE·CUNNING·FOX.

# The Ape.

THERE is an ape in Paris,
    To which was given a wife:
Like many a one that marries,
    This ape, in brutal strife,
    Soon beat her out of life.
Their infant cries,—perhaps not fed,—
    But cries, I ween, in vain;
The father laughs: his wife is dead,
    And he has other loves again,
Which he will also beat, I think,—
Return'd from tavern drown'd in drink.

*For aught that's good, you need not look*
    *Among the imitative tribe;*
*A monkey be it, or what makes a book—*
    *The worse, I deem—the aping scribe.*

## THE ◦APE◦

# The Fox, the Flies, and the Hedgehog.

A FOX, old, subtle, vigilant, and sly,—
   By hunters wounded, fallen in the mud,—
Attracted by the traces of his blood,
   That buzzing parasite, the fly.
   He blamed the gods, and wonder'd why
   The Fates so cruelly should wish
   To feast the fly on such a costly dish.
   "What! light on me! make me its food!
   Me, me, the nimblest of the wood!
   How long has fox-meat been so good?
What serves my tail?   Is it a useless weight?
Go,—Heaven confound thee, greedy reprobate!—
And suck thy fill from some more vulgar veins!"
   A hedgehog, witnessing his pains,
      (This fretful personage
      Here graces first my page,)
      Desired to set him free
      From such cupidity.
      "My neighbour fox," said he,
  " My quills these rascals shall empale,
And ease thy torments without fail."
"Not for the world, my friend!" the fox replied.
  "Pray let them finish their repast.
These flies are full.   Should they be set aside,
  New hungrier swarms would finish me at last."

*Consumers are too common here below,*
*In court and camp, in church and state, we know.*
   *Old Aristotle's penetration*
   *Remark'd our fable's application;*
   *It might more clearly in our nation.*
   *The fuller certain men are fed,*
   *The less the public will be bled.*

**THE·FOX·THE·FLIES·&·THE·HEDGEHOG.**

# The Eagle and the Magpie.

THE eagle, through the air a queen,
　　And one far different, I ween,
In temper, language, thought, and mien,—
The magpie,—once a prairie cross'd.
　　The by-path where they met was drear,
And Madge gave up herself for lost;
　　But having dined on ample cheer,
　　The eagle bade her, "Never fear;
You're welcome to my company;
For if the king of gods can be
　　Full oft in need of recreation,—
Who rules the world,—right well may I,
　　Who serve him in that high relation:
Amuse me, then, before you fly."
Our cackler, pleased, at quickest rate
Of this and that began to prate.
　　No fool, or babbler for that matter,
　　Could more incontinently chatter.
At last she offer'd to make known—
A better spy had never flown—
All things, whatever she might see,
In travelling from tree to tree.
But, with her offer little pleased—
Nay, gathering wrath at being teased,—
For such a purpose, never rove,—
Replied th' impatient bird of Jove.
　　Adieu, my cackling friend, adieu;
My court is not the place for you:
Heaven keep it free from such a bore!"
Madge flapp'd her wings, and said no more.

　　　　'Tis far less easy than it seems
　　　　　　An entrance to the great to gain.
　　　　The honour oft hath cost extremes
　　　　　　Of mortal pain.
　　　　The craft of spies, the tattling art,
　　　　And looks more gracious than the heart,
　　　　　　Are odious there;
　　　　But still, if one would meet success,
　　　　Of different parishes the dress
　　　　　　He, like the pie, must wear.

THE·EAGLE·AND·THE·MAGPIE.

# The Lion and the Hunter.

A BRAGGART, lover of the chase,
   Had lost a dog of valued race,
And thought him in a lion's maw.
He ask'd a shepherd whom he saw,
"Pray show me, man, the robber's place,
And I'll have justice in the case."
   "'Tis on this mountain side,"
   The shepherd man replied.
"The tribute of a sheep I pay,
Each month, and where I please I stray."
   Out leap'd the lion as he spake,
   And came that way with agile feet.
The braggart, prompt his flight to take,
   Cried, "Jove, O grant a safe retreat!"

    *A danger close at hand*
      *Of courage is the test.*
    *It shows us who will stand—*
      *Whose legs will run their best.*

## THE·LION·AND·THE·HUNTER.

# The Fox, the Monkey, and the Animals

LEFT kingless by the lion's death,
　　The beasts once met, our story saith,
Some fit successor to install.
Forth from a dragon-guarded, moated place,
The crown was brought, and, taken from its case,
　　And being tried by turns on all,
　　The heads of most were found too small;
　　Some hornèd were, and some too big;
　　　Not one would fit the regal gear.
For ever ripe for such a rig,
　　The monkey, looking very queer,
Approach'd with antics and grimaces,
And, after scores of monkey faces,
With what would seem a gracious stoop,
Pass'd through the crown as through a hoop.
　　The beasts, diverted with the thing,
　　Did homage to him as their king.
　　The fox alone the vote regretted,
　　But yet in public never fretted.
When he his compliments had paid
To royalty, thus newly made,
"Great sire, I know a place," said he,
　　"Where lies conceal'd a treasure,
Which, by the right of royalty,
　　Should bide your royal pleasure."
The king lack'd not an appetite
　　For such financial pelf,
And, not to lose his royal right,
　　Ran straight to see it for himself.
It was a trap, and he was caught.
Said Renard, "Would you have it thought,
You ape, that you can fill a throne,
And guard the rights of all, alone,
Not knowing how to guard your own?"
*The beasts all gather'd from the farce,*
*That stuff for kings is very scarce.*

**THE·FOX, THE·MONKEY, AND·THE·ANIMALS**

# The Sun and the Frogs.

REJOICING on their tyrant's wedding-day,
  The people drown'd their care in drink;
While from the general joy did Æsop shrink,
  And show'd its folly in this way.
"The sun," said he, "once took it in his head
  To have a partner: so he wed.
From swamps, and ponds, and marshy bogs,
Up rose the wailings of the frogs.
"What shall we do, should he have progeny?"
    Said they to Destiny;
  'One sun we scarcely can endure,
  And half-a-dozen, we are sure,
    Will dry the very sea.
    Adieu to marsh and fen!
    Our race will perish then,
    Or be obliged to fix
    Their dwelling in the Styx!'
For such an humble animal,
  The frog, I take it, reason'd well "

THE·SUN·AND·THE·FROGS···

# The Countryman and the Serpent.

A COUNTRYMAN, as Æsop certifies,
  A charitable man, but not so wise,
One day in winter found,
Stretch'd on the snowy ground,
A chill'd or frozen snake,
As torpid as a stake,
And, if alive, devoid of sense.
He took him up, and bore him home,
  And, thinking not what recompense
For such a charity would come,
    Before the fire stretch'd him,
    And back to being fetch'd him.
  The snake scarce felt the genial heat
Before his heart with native malice beat.
He raised his head, thrust out his forkèd tongue,
Coil'd up, and at his benefactor sprung.
"Ungrateful wretch!" said he, "is this the way
  My care and kindness you repay?
Now you shall die." With that his axe he takes,
And with two blows three serpents makes.
Trunk, head, and tail were separate snakes;
  And, leaping up with all their might,
  They vainly sought to reunite.

  *'Tis good and lovely to be kind;*
  *But charity should not be blind;*
  *For as to wretchedness ingrate,*
*You cannot raise it from its wretched state.*

THE·COUNTRYMAN·AND·THE·SERPENT

# The Carter in the Mire.

THE Phaëton who drove a load of hay
  Once found his cart bemired.
Poor man! the spot was far away
  From human help—retired,
In some rude country place,
In Brittany, as near as I can trace,
  Near Quimper Corentan,—
A town that poet never sang,—
Which Fate, they say, puts in the traveller's path,
When she would rouse the man to special wrath.
May Heaven preserve us from that route!
But to our carter, hale and stout:—
Fast stuck his cart; he swore his worst,
  And, fill'd with rage extreme,
The mud-holes now he cursed,
  And now he cursed his team,
And now his cart and load,—
Anon, the like upon himself bestow'd.
Upon the god he call'd at length,
Most famous through the world for strength.
"O, help me, Hercules!" cried he; "for if thy back of yore
This burly planet bore, thy arm can set me free."
This prayer gone up, from out a cloud there broke
A voice which thus in godlike accents spoke:—
  "The suppliant must himself bestir,
  Ere Hercules will aid confer.
Look wisely in the proper quarter,
  To see what hindrance can be found;
Remove the execrable mud and mortar,
  Which, axle-deep, beset thy wheels around.
Thy sledge and crowbar take,
And pry me up that stone, or break;
Now fill that rut upon the other side.
Hast done it?"   "Yes," the man replied.
"Well," said the voice, "I'll aid thee now;
Take up thy whip."   "I have . . . but, how?
  My cart glides on with ease!
  I thank thee, Hercules."
"Thy team," rejoin'd the voice, "has light ado;
So help thyself, and Heaven will help thee too."

### THE·CARTER·IN·THE·MIRE

# The Heron.

ONE day,—no matter when or where,—
   A long-legg'd heron chanced to fare
By a certain river's brink,
With his long, sharp beak
Helved on his slender neck;
'Twas a fish-spear, you might think.
The water was clear and still,
The carp and the pike there at will
   Pursued their silent fun,
   Turning up, ever and anon,
   A golden side to the sun.
With ease might the heron have made
Great profits in his fishing trade.
So near came the scaly fry,
They might be caught by the passer-by.
But he thought he better might
Wait for a better appetite—
For he lived by rule, and could not eat,
Except at his hours, the best of meat.
Anon his appetite return'd once more;
So, approaching again the shore,
He saw some tench taking their leaps,
Now and then, from their lowest deeps.
With as dainty a taste as Horace's rat,
He turn'd away from such food as that.
"What, tench for a heron! poh!
I scorn the thought, and let them go."
The tench refused, there came a gudgeon;
"For all that," said the bird, "I budge on.
I'll ne'er open my beak, if the gods please,
For such mean little fishes as these."
He did it for less; | For it came to pass,
   That not another fish could he see;
   And, at last, so hungry was he,
   That he thought it of some avail
   To find on the bank a single snail.

*Such is the sure result*     *Would you be strong and great*
*Of being too difficult.*     *Learn to accommodate.*

THE ·HERON·

# The Head and the Tail of the Serpent.

TWO parts the serpent has—
  Of men the enemies—
The head and tail: the same
Have won a mighty fame,
  Next to the cruel Fates;—
 So that, indeed, hence
  They once had great debates
 About precedence.
The first had always gone ahead;
The tail had been for ever led;
And now to Heaven it pray'd,
  And said,
" O, many and many a league,
 Dragg'd on in sore fatigue,
 Behind his back I go.
Shall he for ever use me so?
Am I his humble servant?
No. Thanks to God most fervent!
 His brother I was born,
 And not his slave forlorn.
 The self-same blood in both,
 I'm just as good as he:
 A poison dwells in me
As virulent as doth
In him. In mercy, heed,
 And grant me this decree,
That I, in turn, may lead—
 My brother, follow me.
My course shall be so wise,
That no complaint shall rise."

With cruel kindness Heaven granted
 The very thing he blindly wanted:
  At once this novel guide,
 That saw no more in broad daylight
 Than in the murk of darkest night,
  His powers of leading tried,
Struck trees, and men, and stones, and bricks,
 And led his brother straight to Styx.
  And to the same unlovely home,
  Some states by such an error come.

THE·HEAD·&·THE·TAIL·OF·THE·SERPENT

# The Dog and his Master's Dinner.

OUR eyes are not made proof against the fair,
   Nor hands against the touch of gold.
     Fidelity is sadly rare,
And has been from the days of old.
Well taught his appetite to check,
   And do full many a handy trick,
   A dog was trotting, light and quick,
His master's dinner on his neck.
A temperate, self-denying dog was he,
More than, with such a load, he liked to be.
But still he was, while many such as we
Would not have scrupled to make free.
Strange that to dogs a virtue you may teach,
Which, do your best, to men you vainly preach!
This dog of ours, thus richly fitted out,
A mastiff met, who wish'd the meat, no doubt.
To get it was less easy than he thought:
   The porter laid it down and fought.
   Meantime some other dogs arrive:
   Such dogs are always thick enough,
   And, fearing neither kick nor cuff,
     Upon the public thrive.
Our hero, thus o'ermatch'd and press'd,—
The meat in danger manifest,—
Is fain to share it with the rest;
And, looking very calm and wise,
"No anger, gentlemen," he cries:
"My morsel will myself suffice;
The rest shall be your welcome prize."
With this, the first his charge to violate,
He snaps a mouthful from his freight.
Then follow mastiff, cur, and pup,
Till all is cleanly eaten up.
Not sparingly the party feasted,
And not a dog of all but tasted.

   *In some such manner men abuse*
   *Of towns and states the revenues.*
   *The sheriffs, aldermen, and mayor,*
   *Come in for each a liberal share.*

THE·DOG·AND·HIS·MASTER'S·DINNER·

# The Joker and the Fishes.

A JOKER at a banker's table,
   Most amply spread to satisfy
The height of epicurean wishes,
   Had nothing near but little fishes.
So, taking several of the fry,
He whisper'd to them very nigh,
And seem'd to listen for reply.
The guests much wonder'd what it meant,
And stared upon him all intent.
The joker, then, with sober face,
Politely thus explain'd the case :
" A friend of mine, to India bound,
     Has been, I fear,
     Within a year,
By rocks or tempests wreck'd and drown'd.
I ask'd these strangers from the sea
To tell me where my friend might be.
   But all replied they were too young
To know the least of such a matter—
The older fish could tell me better.
   Pray, may I hear some older tongue ? "
What relish had the gentlefolks
For such a sample of his jokes,
Is more than I can now relate.
They put, I'm sure, upon his plate,
A monster of so old a date,
He must have known the names and fate
Of all the daring voyagers,
Who, following the moon and stars,
Have, by mischances, sunk their bones
Within the realms of Davy Jones ;
And who, for centuries, had seen,
Far down, within the fathomless,
Where whales themselves are sceptreless,
   The ancients in their halls of green.

THE·JOKER
AND
THE·FISHES

# The Rat and the Oyster.

A COUNTRY rat, of little brains,
  Grown weary of inglorious rest,
Left home with all its straws and grains,
  Resolved to know beyond his nest.
When peeping through the nearest fence,
"How big the world is, how immense!"
He cried; "there rise the Alps, and that
Is doubtless famous Ararat."
His mountains were the works of moles,
Or dirt thrown up in digging holes!
Some days of travel brought him where
The tide had left the oysters bare.
Since here our traveller saw the sea,
He thought these shells the ships must be.
"My father was, in truth," said he,
  "A coward, and an ignoramus;
He dared not travel: as for me,
  I've seen the ships and ocean famous;
Have cross'd the deserts without drinking,
And many dangerous streams unshrinking."
Among the shut-up shell-fish, one
Was gaping widely at the sun;
It breathed, and drank the air's perfume,
Expanding, like a flower in bloom.
  Both white and fat, its meat
  Appear'd a dainty treat.
Our rat, when he this shell espied,
Thought for his stomach to provide.
"If not mistaken in the matter,"
Said he, "no meat was ever fatter,
Or in its flavour half so fine,
As that on which to-day I dine."
Thus full of hope, the foolish chap
  Thrust in his head to taste,
And felt the pinching of a trap—
  The oyster closed in haste.

*Now those to whom the world is new*
*Are wonder-struck at every view;*
*And the marauder finds his match,*
*When he is caught who thinks to catch.*

THE
◦ RAT ◦
AND
THE ◦
OYSTER

# The Hog, the Goat, and the Sheep.

A GOAT, a sheep, and porker fat,
    All to the market rode together.
Their own amusement was not that
    Which caused their journey thither.
Their coachman did not mean to "set them down"
To see the shows and wonders of the town.
    The porker cried, in piercing squeals,
    As if with butchers at his heels.
    The other beasts, of milder mood,
    The cause by no means understood.
    They saw no harm, and wonder'd why
    At such a rate the hog should cry.
    "Hush there, old piggy!" said the man,
    "And keep as quiet as you can.
    What wrong have you to squeal about,
    And raise this dev'lish, deaf'ning shout?
    These stiller persons at your side
    Have manners much more dignified.
        Pray, have you heard
        A single word
    Come from that gentleman in wool?
    That proves him wise."  "That proves him fool!"
        The testy hog replied;
        "For did he know
        To what we go,
    He'd cry almost to split his throat;
    So would her ladyship the goat.
    They only think to lose with ease,
    The goat her milk, the sheep his fleece:
    They're, maybe, right; but as for me
    This ride is quite another matter.
    Of service only on the platter,
    My death is quite a certainty.
    Adieu, my dear old piggery!"
    The porker's logic proved at once
    Himself a prophet and a dunce.

*Hope ever gives a present ease,*   *The wisest he who least foresees*
  *But fear beforehand kills:*     *Inevitable ills.*

**THE·HOG·THE·GOAT·AND·THE·SHEEP.**

# The Rat and the Elephant.

A RAT, of quite the smallest size,
  Fix'd on an elephant his eyes,
And jeer'd the beast of high descent
Because his feet so slowly went.
Upon his back, three stories high,
There sat, beneath a canopy,
A certain sultan of renown,
  His dog, and cat, and wife sublime,
  His parrot, servant, and his wine,
All pilgrims to a distant town.
The rat profess'd to be amazed
That all the people stood and gazed
With wonder, as he pass'd the road,
Both at the creature and his load.
"As if," said he, "to occupy
A little more of land or sky
Made one, in view of common sense,
  Of greater worth and consequence!
What see ye, men, in this parade,
That food for wonder need be made?
The bulk which makes a child afraid?
In truth, I take myself to be,
In all aspects, as good as he."
And further might have gone his vaunt;
  But, darting down, the cat
  Convinced him that a rat
Is smaller than an elephant.

## THE·RAT·AND·THE·ELEPHANT

# The Ass and the Dog.

ALONG the road an ass and dog
   One master following, did jog.
Their master slept : meanwhile, the ass
Applied his nippers to the grass,
Much pleased in such a place to stop,
Though there no thistle he could crop.
He would not be too delicate,
Nor spoil a dinner for a plate,
Which, but for that, his favourite dish,
Were all that any ass could wish.
   "My dear companion," Towser said,—
"'Tis as a starving dog I ask it,—
Pray lower down your loaded basket,
   And let me get a piece of bread."
No answer—not a word !—indeed,
The truth was, our Arcadian steed
Fear'd lest, for every moment's flight,
His nimble teeth should lose a bite.
At last, "I counsel you," said he, "to wait
   Till master is himself awake,
   Who then, unless I much mistake,
Will give his dog the usual bait."
Meanwhile, there issued from the wood
A creature of the wolfish brood,
Himself by famine sorely pinch'd.
At sight of him the donkey flinch'd,
And begg'd the dog to give him aid.
The dog budged not, but answer made,—
"I counsel thee, my friend, to run,
Till master's nap is fairly done ;
There can, indeed, be no mistake,
That he will very soon awake ;
Till then, scud off with all your might ;
And should he snap you in your flight,
This ugly wolf,—why, let him feel
The greeting of your well-shod heel.
I do not doubt, at all, but that
Will be enough to lay him flat."
   But ere he ceased it was too late ;
   The ass had met his cruel fate.

THE·ASS·AND·THE·DOG···

# Education.

LAPLUCK and Cæsar brothers were, descended
  From dogs by Fame the most commended,
Who falling, in their puppyhood,
  To different masters anciently,
One dwelt and hunted in the boundless wood;
  From thieves the other kept a kitchen free.
    At first, each had another name;
    But, by their bringing up, it came,
While one improved upon his nature,
The other grew a sordid creature,
    Till, by some scullion called Lapluck,
    The name ungracious ever stuck.
      To high exploits his brother grew,
    Put many a stag at bay, and tore
    Full many a trophy from the boar;
      In short, him first, of all his crew,
        The world as Cæsar knew;
And care was had, lest, by a baser mate,
His noble blood should e'er degenerate.
Not so with him of lower station,
Whose race became a countless nation—
The common turnspits throughout France—
Where danger is, they don't advance—
Precisely the Antipodes
Of what we call the Cæsars, these!

*Oft falls the son below his sire's estate:*
*Through want of care all things degenerate.*
*For lack of nursing Nature and her gifts,*
*What crowds from gods become mere kitchen-thrifts !*

**EDUCATION.**

# The Two Dogs and the Dead Ass.

TWO lean and hungry mastiffs once espied
   A dead ass floating on a water wide.
The distance growing more and more,
Because the wind the carcass bore,—
" My friend," said one, " your eyes are best ;
Pray let them on the water rest :
What thing is that I seem to see ?
An ox, or horse ? what can it be ? "
"Hey ! " cried his mate ; " what matter which,
Provided we could get a flitch ?
It doubtless is our lawful prey :
The puzzle is to find some way
To get the prize ; for wide the space
To swim, with wind against your face.
Let's drink the flood ; our thirsty throats
Will gain the end as well as boats.
The water swallow'd, by and by
We'll have the carcass, high and dry—
Enough to last a week, at least."
Both drank as some do at a feast ;
Their breath was quench'd before their thirst,
And presently the creatures burst !

*And such is man.   Whatever he*
*May set his soul to do or be,*
*To him is possibility.*
   *How many vows he makes !*
   *How many steps he takes !*
*How does he strive, and pant, and strain,*
*Fortune's or Glory's prize to gain !*

## THE·TWO·DOGS·AND·THE·DEAD·ASS

# The Monkey and the Leopard.

A MONKEY and a leopard were
    The rivals at a country fair.
Each advertised his own attractions.
    Said one, "Good sirs, the highest place
    My merit knows; for, of his grace,
    The king hath seen me face to face;
And, judging by his looks and actions,
I gave the best of satisfactions.
When I am dead, 'tis plain enough,
My skin will make his royal muff.
So richly is it streak'd and spotted,
So delicately waved and dotted,
Its various beauty cannot fail to please."
And, thus invited, everybody sees;
But soon they see, and soon depart.
The monkey's show-bill to the mart
His merits thus sets forth the while,
All in his own peculiar style :—
"Come, gentlemen, I pray you, come;
In magic arts I am at home.
The whole variety in which
My neighbour boasts himself so rich,
Is to his simple skin confined,
While mine is living in the mind.
For I can speak, you understand;
    Can dance, and practise sleight-of-hand;
Can jump through hoops, and balance sticks;
In short, can do a thousand tricks;
    One penny is my charge to you,
    And, if you think the price won't do,
    When you have seen, then I'll restore
Each man his money at the door."
*The ape was not to reason blind;*
*For who in wealth of dress can find*
*Such charms as dwell in wealth of mind?*
*One meets our ever-new desires,*
*The other in a moment tires.*
*Alas! how many lords there are,*
    *Of mighty sway and lofty mien,*
*Who, like this leopard at the fair,*
    *Show all their talents on the skin!*

THE·MONKEY·AND·THE·LEOPARD·

# The Acorn and the Pumpkin.

GOD'S works are good.  This truth to prove
   Around the world I need not move ;
I do it by the nearest pumpkin.
"This fruit so large, on vine so small,"
   Surveying once, exclaim'd a bumpkin—
"What could He mean who made us all ?
He's left this pumpkin out of place.
If I had order'd in the case,
Upon that oak it should have hung—
A noble fruit as ever swung
To grace a tree so firm and strong.
Indeed, it was a great mistake,
    As this discovery teaches,
That I myself did not partake
His counsels whom my curate preaches.
All things had then in order come ;
   This acorn, for example,
    Not bigger than my thumb,
Had not disgraced a tree so ample.
The more I think, the more I wonder
To see outraged proportion's laws,
And that without the slightest cause ;
God surely made an awkward blunder."
With such reflections proudly fraught,
Our sage grew tired of mighty thought,
And threw himself on Nature's lap,
Beneath an oak, to take his nap.
Plump on his nose, by lucky hap,
An acorn fell : he waked, and in
The scarf he wore beneath his chin,
He found the cause of such a bruise
As made him different language use.
"O ! O !" he cried ; "I bleed ! I bleed !
And this is what has done the deed !
But, truly, what had been my fate,
Had this had half a pumpkin's weight !
I see that God had reasons good,
And all His works were understood."
Thus home he went in humbler mood.

THE·ACORN·AND·THE·PUMPKIN

# The Fool who Sold Wisdom.

A FOOL, in town, did wisdom cry;
    The people, eager, flock'd to buy.
Each for his money got,
Paid promptly on the spot,
Besides a box upon the head,
Two fathoms' length of thread.
The most were vex'd—but quite in vain,
The public only mock'd their pain.
The wiser they who nothing said,
But pocketed the box and thread.
To search the meaning of the thing
Would only laughs and hisses bring.
Hath reason ever guaranteed
The wit of fools in speech or deed?
'Tis said of brainless heads in France,
The cause of what they do is chance.
One dupe, however, needs must know
What meant the thread, and what the blow
So ask'd a sage, to make it sure.
" They're both hieroglyphics pure,"
The sage replied without delay;
" All people well advised will stay
From fools this fibre's length away,
Or get—I hold it sure as fate—
The other symbol on the pate.
So far from cheating you of gold,
The fool this wisdom fairly sold."

THE·FOOL·WHO·SOLD·WISDOM···

# The Oyster and the Litigants.

TWO pilgrims on the sand espied
   An oyster thrown up by the tide.
In hope, both swallow'd ocean's fruit;
But ere the fact there came dispute.
While one stoop'd down to take the prey,
The other push'd him quite away.
   Said he, "'Twere rather meet
   To settle which shall eat.
Why, he who first the oyster saw
Should be its eater by the law;
The other should but see him do it."
Replied his mate, "If thus you view it,
Thank God the lucky eye is mine."
"But I've an eye not worse than thine,"
The other cried, "and will be cursed,
If, too, I didn't see it first."
"You saw it, did you?  Grant it true,
I saw it then, and felt it too."
     Amidst this sweet affair,
    Arrived a person very big,
    Ycleped Sir Nincom Periwig.
They made him judge,—to set the matter square.
   Sir Nincom, with a solemn face,
   Took up the oyster and the case:
   In opening both, the first he swallow'd,
   And, in due time, his judgment follow'd.
"Attend: the court awards you each a shell
Cost free; depart in peace, and use them well.'

*Foot up the cost of suits at law,*
*The leavings reckon and awards,*
*The cash you'll see Sir Nincom draw,*
*And leave the parties—purse and cards.*

THE·OYSTER·AND·THE·LITIGANTS.

# The Wolf and the Lean Dog.

A TROUTLING, some time since,
   Endeavour'd vainly to convince
A hungry fisherman
Of his unfitness for the frying-pan.
The fisherman had reason good—
The troutling did the best he could—
   Both argued for their lives.
Now, if my present purpose thrives,
I'll prop my former proposition
By building on a small addition.
   A certain wolf, in point of wit
   The prudent fisher's opposite,
   A dog once finding far astray,
   Prepared to take him as his prey.
     The dog his leanness pled ;
     " Your lordship, sure," he said,
     " Cannot be very eager
     To eat a dog so meagre.
   To wait a little do not grudge :
The wedding of my master's only daughter
Will cause of fatted calves and fowls a slaughter ;
   And then, as you yourself can judge,
   I cannot help becoming fatter."
The wolf, believing, waived the matter,
And so, some days therefrom,
   Return'd with sole design to see
   If fat enough his dog might be.
The rogue was now at home :
He saw the hunter through the fence.
   " My friend," said he, " please wait ;
I'll be with you a moment hence,
   And fetch our porter of the gate."
This porter was a dog immense,
That left to wolves no future tense.
   Suspicion gave our wolf a jog,—
   It might not be so safely tamper'd.
   " My service to your porter dog,"
Was his reply, as off he scamper'd.
His legs proved better than his head,
And saved him life to learn his trade.

**THE·WOLF·AND·THE·LEAN·DOG.**

# Nothing too Much.

LOOK where we will throughout creation,
  We look in vain for moderation.
The grain, best gift of Ceres fair,
Green waving in the genial air,
By overgrowth exhausts the soil;
  By superfluity of leaves
  Defrauds the treasure of its sheaves,
And mocks the busy farmer's toil.
Not less redundant is the tree,
So sweet a thing is luxury.
The grain within due bounds to keep,
Their Maker licenses the sheep
The leaves excessive to retrench.
  In troops they spread across the plain,
  And, nibbling down the hapless grain,
Contrive to spoil it, root and branch.
  So, then, with licence from on high,
The wolves are sent on sheep to prey;
The whole the greedy gluttons slay;
  Or, if they don't, they try.

Next, men are sent on wolves to take
  The vengeance now condign:
In turn the same abuse they make
  Of this behest divine.

Of animals, the human kind
Are to excess the most inclined.
On low and high we make the charge,—
Indeed, upon the race at large.
There liveth not the soul select
That sinneth not in this respect.
Of "Nought too much," the fact is,
All preach the truth,—none practise.

**NOTHING·TOO·MUCH.**

# The Cat and the Fox.

THE cat and fox, when saints were all the rage
    Together went upon pilgrimage.
Our pilgrims, as a thing of course,
Disputed till their throats were hoarse.
    Then, dropping to a lower tone,
They talk'd of this, and talk'd of that,
Till Renard whisper'd to the cat,
    "You think yourself a knowing one:
How many cunning tricks have you?
For I've a hundred, old and new,
All ready in my haversack."
The cat replied, "I do not lack,
    Though with but one provided;
And, truth to honour, for that matter,
I hold it than a thousand better."
    In fresh dispute they sided;
And loudly were they at it, when
Approach'd a mob of dogs and men.
"Now," said the cat, "your tricks ransack,
And put your cunning brains to rack,
One life to save; I'll show you mine—
A trick, you see, for saving nine."
With that, she climb'd a lofty pine.
The fox his hundred ruses tried,
    And yet no safety found.
A hundred times he falsified
    The nose of every hound.—
Was here, and there, and everywhere,
    Above, and under ground;
But yet to stop he did not dare,
Pent in a hole, it was no joke,
To meet the terriers or the smoke.
So, leaping into upper air,
He met two dogs, that choked him there.

*Expedients may be too many,*     *On one, but that as good as any,*
*Consuming time to choose and try.*   *'Tis best in danger to rely.*

THE·CAT·AND·THE·FOX.

# The Monkey and the Cat.

SLY Bertrand and Ratto in company sat,
    (The one was a monkey, the other a cat,)
    Co-servants and lodgers:
    More mischievous codgers
Ne'er mess'd from a platter, since platters were flat.
Was anything wrong in the house or about it,
The neighbours were blameless,—no mortal could
    doubt it;
For Bertrand was thievish, and Ratto so nice,
More attentive to cheese than he was to the mice.
One day the two plunderers sat by the fire,
Where chestnuts were roasting, with looks of desire.
To steal them would be a right noble affair.
A double inducement our heroes drew there—
'Twould benefit them, could they swallow their fill,
And then 'twould occasion to somebody ill.
Said Bertrand to Ratto, " My brother, to-day
Exhibit your powers in a masterly way,
    And take me these chestnuts, I pray.
    Which were I but otherwise fitted
    (As I am ingeniously witted)
    For pulling things out of the flame,
    Would stand but a pitiful game."
" 'Tis done," replied Ratto, all prompt to obey;
And thrust out his paw in a delicate way.
    First giving the ashes a scratch,
    He open'd the coveted batch;
    Then lightly and quickly impinging,
    He drew out, in spite of the singeing,
One after another, the chestnuts at last,—
While Bertrand contrived to devour them as fast.
    A servant girl enters.   Adieu to the fun.
    Our Ratto was hardly contented, says one.—

*No more are the princes, by flattery paid*
*For furnishing help in a different trade,*
    *And burning their fingers to bring*
    *More power to some mightier king.*

**THE·MONKEY·AND·THE·CAT.**

# The Spider and the Swallow.

"O JUPITER, whose fruitful brain,
  By odd obstetrics freed from pain,
Bore Pallas, erst my mortal foe,
Pray listen to my tale of woe.
This Progne takes my lawful prey.
As through the air she cuts her way,
My flies she catches from my door,—
    Yes, *mine*—I emphasize the word,—
    And, but for this accursed bird,
My net would hold an ample store:
For I have woven it of stuff
To hold the strongest strong enough."
'Twas thus, in terms of insolence,
Complain'd the fretful spider, once
    Of palace-tapestry a weaver,
    But then a spinster and deceiver,
That hoped within her toils to bring
Of insects all that ply the wing.
The sister swift of Philomel,
Intent on business, prosper'd well;
In spite of the complaining pest,
The insects carried to her nest—
Nest pitiless to suffering flies—
Mouths gaping aye, to gormandize,
    Of young ones clamouring,
        And stammering,
With unintelligible cries.
The spider, with but head and feet,
    And powerless to compete
    With wings so fleet,
    Soon saw herself a prey.
The swallow, passing swiftly by,
    Bore web and all away,
The spinster dangling in the sky!

*Two tables hath our Maker set*
*For all that in this world are met.*
    *To seats around the first*
*The skilful, vigilant, and strong are beckon'd :*
    *Their hunger and their thirst*
*The rest must quell with leavings at the second.*

**THE·SPIDER·AND·THE·SWALLOW.**

# The Dog whose Ears were Cropped.

"WHAT have I done, I'd like to know,
  To make my master maim me so?
A pretty figure I shall cut!
From other dogs I'll keep, in kennel shut.
Ye kings of beasts, or rather tyrants, ho!
  Would any beast have served you so?"
  Thus Growler cried, a mastiff young;—
  The man, whom pity never stung,
    Went on to prune him of his ears.
Though Growler whined about his losses,
    He found, before the lapse of years,
Himself a gainer by the process;
  For, being by his nature prone
  To fight his brethren for a bone,
  He'd oft come back from sad reverse
  With those appendages the worse.
    All snarling dogs have ragged ears.

The less of hold for teeth of foe,
The better will the battle go.
  When, in a certain place, one fears
The chance of being hurt or beat,
He fortifies it from defeat.
  Besides the shortness of his ears,
See Growler arm'd against his likes
With gorget full of ugly spikes.
A wolf would find it quite a puzzle
To get a hold about his muzzle.

THE·DOG·WHOSE·EARS·WERE·CROPPED

# The Lioness and the Bear.

THE lioness had lost her young;
  A hunter stole it from the vale;
The forests and the mountains rung
  Responsive to her hideous wail.
Nor night, nor charms of sweet repose,
Could still the loud lament that rose
    From that grim forest queen.
No animal, as you might think,
With such a noise could sleep a wink.
    A bear presumed to intervene.
    " One word, sweet friend," quoth she,
    " And that is all, from me.
The young that through your teeth have pass'd,
  In file unbroken by a fast,
      Had they nor dam nor sire ? "
    " They had them both."  " Then I desire,
Since all their deaths caused no such grievous riot,
While mothers died of grief beneath your fiat,
To know why you yourself cannot be quiet ? "
    " I quiet !—I !—a wretch bereaved !
My only son !—such anguish be relieved !
No, never !  All for me below
Is but a life of tears and woe ! "—
" But say, why doom yourself to sorrow so ? "—
" Alas ! 'tis Destiny that is my foe."

  *Such language, since the mortal fall,*
  *Has fallen from the lips of all.*
  *Ye human wretches, give your heed;*
  *For your complaints there's little need.*
*Let him who thinks his own the hardest case,*
  *Some widowed, childless Hecuba behold,*
  *Herself to toil and shame of slavery sold,*
*And he will own the wealth of heavenly grace.*

146

THE·LIONESS·AND·THE·BEAR.

# The Mice and the Owl.

A PINE was by a woodman fell'd,
  Which ancient, huge, and hollow tree
An owl had for his palace held—
  A bird the Fates had kept in fee,
  Interpreter to such as we.
Within the caverns of the pine,
With other tenants of that mine,
Were found full many footless mice,
But well provision'd, fat, and nice.
The bird had bit off all their feet,
And fed them there with heaps of wheat.
That this owl reason'd, who can doubt?
When to the chase he first went out,
And home alive the vermin brought,
Which in his talons he had caught,
The nimble creatures ran away.
Next time, resolved to make them stay,
He cropp'd their legs, and found, with pleasure,
That he could eat them at his leisure;
  It were impossible to eat
  Them all at once, did health permit.
His foresight, equal to our own,
In furnishing their food was shown.
Now, let Cartesians, if they can,
  Pronounce this owl a mere machine.
Could springs originate the plan
  Of maiming mice when taken lean,
  To fatten for his soup-tureen?
If reason did no service there,
I do not know it anywhere.
  Observe the course of argument:
These vermin are no sooner caught than gone:
  They must be used as soon, 'tis evident;
  But this to all cannot be done.
    Hence, while their ribs I lard,
    I must from their elopement guard.
    But how?—A plan complete!—
    I'll clip them of their feet!
Now, find me, in your human schools,
A better use of logic's tools!

148

**THE·MICE·AND·THE·OWL·**

# The Cat and the Two Sparrows.

CONTEMPORARY with a sparrow tame
    There lived a cat; from tenderest age,
Of both, the basket and the cage
    Had household gods the same.
The bird's sharp beak full oft provoked the cat,
Who play'd in turn, but with a gentle pat,
His wee friend sparing with a merry laugh,
Not punishing his faults by half.
    In short, he scrupled much the harm,
    Should he with points his ferule arm.
    The Sparrow, less discreet than he,
    With dagger beak made very free.
    Sir Cat, a person wise and staid,
    Excused the warmth with which he play'd:
       For 'tis full half of friendship's art
       To take no joke in serious part.
       Familiar since they saw the light,
         Mere habit kept their friendship good;
       Fair play had never turn'd to fight,
         Till, of their neighbourhood,
    Another sparrow came to greet
    Old Ratto grave and Saucy Pete.
    Between the birds a quarrel rose,
       And Ratto took his side.
    "A pretty stranger, with such blows
       To beat our friend!" he cried.
    "A neighbour's sparrow eating ours!
    Not so, by all the feline powers."
    And quick the stranger he devours.
       "Now, truly," saith Sir Cat,
    "I know how sparrows taste by that.
    Exquisite, tender, delicate!"
    This thought soon seal'd the other's fate.—
    But hence what moral can I bring?
    For, lacking that important thing,
    A fable lacks its finishing:
    I seem to see of one some trace,
    But still its shadow mocks my chase.

THE·CAT·AND·THE·TWO·SPARROWS

# The Two Goats.

TWO goats, who self-emancipated,—
　　The white that on their feet they wore
Look'd back to noble blood of yore,—
　　Once quit the lowly meadows, sated,
And sought the hills, as it would seem :
　　In search of luck, by luck they met
Each other at a mountain stream.
　　As bridge a narrow plank was set,
On which, if truth must be confest,
Two weasels scarce could go abreast.
And then the torrent, foaming white,
As down it tumbled from the height,
Might well those Amazons affright.
But maugre such a fearful rapid,
Both took the bridge, the goats intrepid !
　　I seem to see our Louis Grand
　　　　And Philip IV. advance
　　　　To the Isle of Conference,
　　　　That lies 'twixt Spain and France,
　　Each sturdy for his glorious land.
　　Thus each of our adventurers goes,
　　Till foot to foot, and nose to nose,
　　Somewhere about the midst they meet,
　　And neither will an inch retreat.
For why ? they both enjoy'd the glory
Of ancestors in ancient story.
　　The one, a goat of peerless rank,
　　Which, browsing on Sicilian bank,
　　The Cyclop gave to Galatæa ;
　　The other famous Amalthæa,
　　The goat that suckled Jupiter,
　　As some historians aver.
　　For want of giving back, in troth,
　　A common fall involved them both.—
　　A common accident, no doubt,
　　On Fortune's changeful route.

## THE·TWO·GOATS

# The Old Cat and the Young Mouse.

A YOUNG and inexperienced mouse
    Had faith to try a veteran cat,—
Raminagrobis, death to rat,
And scourge of vermin through the house,—
Appealing to his clemency
    With reasons sound and fair.
"Pray let me live; a mouse like me
    It were not much to spare.
Am I, in such a family,
A burden? Would my largest wish
Our wealthy host impoverish?
A grain of wheat will make my meal;
A nut will fat me like a seal.
I'm lean at present; please to wait,
And for your heirs reserve my fate."
    The captive mouse thus spake.
Replied the captor, "You mistake;
To me shall such a thing be said?
Address the deaf! address the dead!
A cat to pardon!—old one too!
Why, such a thing I never knew.
    Thou victim of my paw,
    By well-establish'd law,
    Die as a mousling should,
    And beg the sisterhood
    Who ply the thread and shears,
    To lend thy speech their ears.
Some other like repast
My heirs may find, or fast."

He ceased. The moral's plain.
*Youth always hopes its ends to gain,*
*Believes all spirits like its own:*
*Old age is not to mercy prone.*

THE·OLD·CAT·AND·THE·YOUNG·MOUSE

# The Sick Stag.

A STAG, where stags abounded,
   Fell sick and was surrounded
Forthwith by comrades kind,
  All pressing to assist,
  Or see, their friend, at least,
And ease his anxious mind—
  An irksome multitude.
"Ah, sirs!" the sick was fain to cry,
"Pray leave me here to die,
  As others do, in solitude.
Pray, let your kind attentions cease,
Till death my spirit shall release."
But comforters are not so sent:
On duty sad full long intent,
When Heaven pleased, they went:
But not without a friendly glass;
That is to say, they cropp'd the grass
And leaves which in that quarter grew,
From which the sick his pittance drew.
By kindness thus compell'd to fast,
He died for want of food at last.

*The men take off no trifling dole*
*Who heal the body, or the soul.*
*Alas the times! do what we will,*
*They have their payment, cure or kill.*

THE·SICK·STAG.

# The Quarrel of the Dogs and Cats.

IN mansion deck'd with frieze and column,
  Dwelt dogs and cats in multitudes;
Decrees, promulged in manner solemn,
  Had pacified their ancient feuds.
Their lord had so arranged their meals and labours,
  And threaten'd quarrels with the whip,
  That, living in sweet cousinship,
They edified their wondering neighbours.
  At last, some dainty plate to lick,
  Or profitable bone to pick,
  Bestow'd by some partiality,
  Broke up the smooth equality.
  The side neglected were indignant
  At such a slight malignant.
  From words to blows the altercation
  Soon grew a perfect conflagration.
In hall and kitchen, dog and cat
  Took sides with zeal for this or that.
  New rules upon the cat side falling
  Produced tremendous caterwauling.
Their advocate, against such rules as these,
Advised recurrence to the old decrees.
They search'd in vain, for, hidden in a nook,
The thievish mice had eaten up the book.
  Another quarrel, in a trice,
  Made many sufferers with the mice;
  For many a veteran whisker'd-face,
With craft and cunning richly stored,
  And grudges old against the race,
Now watch'd to put them to the sword;
Nor mourn'd for this that mansion's lord.

*Look wheresoe'er we will, we see*
*No creature from opponents free.*
*'Tis nature's law for earth and sky;*
*'Twere vain to ask the reason why:*
*God's works are good,—I cannot doubt it,—*
*And that is all I know about it.*

**THE·QUARREL·OF·THE·DOGS·AND·CATS.**

# The Wolf and the Fox.

"DEAR wolf," complain'd a hungry fox,
   "A lean chick's meat, or veteran cock's,
Is all I get by toil or trick:
Of such a living I am sick.
With far less risk, you've better cheer;
A house you need not venture near,
But I must do it, spite of fear.
Pray, make me master of your trade.
And let me by that means be made
The first of all my race that took
Fat mutton to his larder's hook:
Your kindness shall not be repented."
The wolf quite readily consented.
"I have a brother, lately dead:
Go fit his skin to yours," he said.
'Twas done; and then the wolf proceeded:
   "Now mark you well what must be done,
The dogs that guard the flock to shun."
The fox the lessons strictly heeded.
   At first he boggled in his dress;
But awkwardness grew less and less,
Till perseverance gave success.
His education scarce complete,
A flock, his scholarship to greet,
   Came rambling out that way.
The new-made wolf his work began,
Amidst the heedless nibblers ran,
   And spread a sore dismay.
The bleating host now surely thought
That fifty wolves were on the spot:
   Dog, shepherd, sheep, all homeward fled,
And left a single sheep in pawn,
Which Renard seized when they were gone.
   But, ere upon his prize he fed,
There crow'd a cock near by, and down
The scholar threw his prey and gown,
That he might run that way the faster—
Forgetting lessons, prize and master.

    *Reality, in every station,*
    *Will burst out on the first occasion.*

THE·WOLF·AND·THE·FOX···

# The Lobster and her Daughter.

THE wise, sometimes, as lobsters do,
 To gain their ends back foremost go.
It is the rower's art; and those
Commanders who mislead their foes,
Do often seem to aim their sight
Just where they don't intend to smite.
My theme, so low, may yet apply
To one whose fame is very high,
 Who finds it not the hardest matter
 A hundred-headed league to scatter.
What he will do, what leave undone,
 Are secrets with unbroken seals,
 Till victory the truth reveals.
Whatever he would have unknown
Is sought in vain.   Decrees of Fate
Forbid to check, at first, the course
Which sweeps at last the torrent force.
 One Jove, as ancient fables state,
 Exceeds a hundred gods in weight.
So Fate and Louis would seem able
 The universe to draw,
 Bound captive to their law.—
But come we to our fable.
A mother lobster did her daughter chide:
"For shame, my daughter! can't you go ahead?"
 "And how go you yourself?" the child replied;
"Can I be but by your example led?
 Head foremost should I, singularly, wend,
 While all my race pursue the other end."
She spoke with sense: for better or for worse,
 Example has a universal force.
 To some it opens wisdom's door,
 But leads to folly many more.
 Yet, as for backing to one's aim,
 When properly pursued
 The art is doubtless good,
At least in grim Bellona's game.

THE·LOBSTER·AND·HER·DAUGHTER

# The Ploughman and his Sons.

*The farmer's patient care and toil*
*Are oftener wanting than the soil.*

A WEALTHY ploughman drawing near his end,
  Call'd in his sons apart from every friend,
And said, "When of your sire bereft,
The heritage our fathers left
Guard well, nor sell a single field.
A treasure in it is conceal'd :
The place, precisely, I don't know,
But industry will serve to show.
The harvest past, Time's forelock take,
And search with plough, and spade, and rake ;
Turn over every inch of sod,
Nor leave unsearch'd a single clod."
The father died.   The sons—and not in vain—
Turn'd o'er the soil, and o'er again ;
That year their acres bore
More grain than e'er before.
Though hidden money found they none,
Yet had their father wisely done,
    To show by such a measure,
    That toil itself is treasure.

THE·PLOUGHMAN·AND·HIS·SONS···

# The Ass Dressed in the Lion's Skin.

CLAD in a lion's shaggy hide,
    An ass spread terror far and wide,
And, though himself a coward brute,
Put all the world to scampering rout :
    But, by a piece of evil luck,
    A portion of an ear outstuck,
    Which soon reveal'd the error
    Of all the panic terror.
Old Martin did his office quick.
Surprised were all who did not know the trick,
    To see that Martin, at his will,
    Was driving lions to the mill !

    *In France, the men are not a few*
    *Of whom this fable proves too true ;*
    *Whose valour chiefly doth reside*
    *In coat they wear and horse they ride.*

THE·ASS·DRESSED·IN·THE·LION'S·SKIN

# The Woods and the Woodman.

A CERTAIN wood-chopper lost or broke
  From his axe's eye a bit of oak.
The forest must needs be somewhat spared
While such a loss was being repair'd.
Came the man at last, and humbly pray'd
 That the woods would kindly lend to him—
 A moderate loan—a single limb,
Whereof might another helve be made,
And his axe should elsewhere drive its trade.
O, the oaks and firs that then might stand,
A pride and a joy throughout the land,
For their ancientness and glorious charms!
The innocent Forest lent him arms;
But bitter indeed was her regret;
For the wretch, his axe new-helved and whet,
Did nought but his benefactress spoil
Of the finest trees that graced her soil;
And ceaselessly was she made to groan,
Doing penance for that fatal loan.

 *Behold the world-stage and its actors,*
 *Where benefits hurt benefactors!—*
  *A weary theme, and full of pain;*
 *For where's the shade so cool and sweet,*
 *Protecting strangers from the heat,*
  *But might of such a wrong complain?*
  *Alas! I vex myself in vain;*
  *Ingratitude, do what I will,*
  *Is sure to be the fashion still.*

## THE·WOODS·AND·THE·WOODMAN.

# The Fox, the Wolf, and the Horse.

A FOX, though young, by no means raw,
   Had seen a horse, the first he ever saw:
"Ho! neighbour wolf," said he to one quite green,
"A creature in our meadow I have seen,—
   Sleek, grand! I seem to see him yet,—
   The finest beast I ever met."
    "Is he a stouter one than we?"
   Tne wolf demanded, eagerly;
   "Some picture of him let me see."
"If I could paint," said fox, "I should delight
T' anticipate your pleasure at the sight;
But come; who knows? perhaps it is a prey
   By fortune offer'd in our way."
  They went.  The horse, turn'd loose to graze,
  Not liking much their looks and ways,
    Was just about to gallop off.
"Sir," said the fox, "your humble servants, we
Make bold to ask you what your name may be."
  The horse, an animal with brains enough,
Replied, "Sirs, you yourselves may read my name;
My shoer round my heel hath writ the same."
The fox excus'd himself for want of knowledge:
  "Me, sir, my parents did not educate,—
So poor, a hole was their entire estate.
My friend, the wolf, however, taught at college,
    Could read it were it even Greek."
    The wolf, to flattery weak,
   Approach'd to verify the boast;
   For which four teeth he lost.
The high raised hoof came down with such a blow,
As laid him bleeding on the ground full low.
"My brother," said the fox, "this shows how just
  What once was taught me by a fox of wit,—
  Which on thy jaws this animal hath writ,—
'All unknown things the wise mistrust.'"

THE·FOX·THE·WOLF·AND·THE·HORSE.

# The Fox and the Turkeys.

AGAINST a robber fox, a tree
    Some turkeys served as citadel.
That villain, much provoked to see
    Each standing there as sentinel,
      Cried out, "Such witless birds
At me stretch out their necks, and gobble!
No, by the powers! I'll give them trouble."
    He verified his words.
The moon, that shined full on the oak,
Seem'd then to help the turkey folk.
But fox, in arts of siege well versed,
Ransack'd his bag of tricks accursed.
He feign'd himself about to climb;
Walk'd on his hinder legs sublime;
Then death most aptly counterfeited,
And seem'd anon resuscitated.
    A practiser of wizard arts
    Could not have fill'd so many parts.
In moonlight he contrived to raise
His tail, and make it seem a blaze:
And countless other tricks like that.
Meanwhile, no turkey slept or sat.
Their constant vigilance at length,
As hoped the fox, wore out their strength.
Bewilder'd by the rigs he run,
They lost their balance one by one.
As Renard slew, he laid aside,
Till nearly half of them had died;
Then proudly to his larder bore,
And laid them up, an ample store.

*A foe, by being over-heeded,*
*Has often in his plan succeeded.*

THE·FOX·AND·THE·TURKEYS.

# The Wallet.

FROM heaven, one day, did Jupiter proclaim,
   "Let all that live before my throne appear,
And there if any one hath aught to blame,
In matter, form, or texture of his frame,
   He may bring forth his grievance without fear.
Redress shall instantly be given to each.
Come, monkey, now, first let us have your speech.
   You see these quadrupeds, your brothers;
   Comparing, then, yourself with others,
   Are you well satisfied?"  "And wherefore not?"
Says Jock.  "Haven't I four trotters with the rest?
Is not my visage comely as the best?
   But this my brother Bruin, is a blot
     On thy creation fair;
   And sooner than be painted I'd be shot,
     Were I, great sire, a bear."
The bear approaching, doth he make complaint?
Not he;—himself he lauds without restraint.
   The elephant he needs must criticise;
   To crop his ears and stretch his tail were wise;
   A creature he of huge, misshapen size.
The elephant, though famed as beast judicious,
While on his own account he had no wishes,
Pronounced dame whale too big to suit his taste;
Of flesh and fat she was a perfect waste.
The little ant, again, pronounced the gnat too wee;
To such a speck, a vast colossus she.
Each censured by the rest, himself content,
Back to their homes all living things were sent.

   *Such folly liveth yet with human fools.*
   *For others lynxes, for ourselves but moles.*
   *Great blemishes in other men we spy,*
   *Which in ourselves we pass most kindly by.*
   *As in this world we're but way-farers,*
   *Kind Heaven has made us wallet-bearers.*
   *The pouch behind our own defects must store,*
   *The faults of others lodge in that before.*

**THE·WALLET.**

# The Woodman and Mercury.

A MAN that labour'd in the wood
    Had lost his honest livelihood;
      That is to say,
  His axe was gone astray.
  He had no tools to spare;
  This wholly earn'd his fare.
  Without a hope beside,
  He sat him down and cried,
"Alas, my axe! where can it be?
O Jove! but send it back to me,
And it shall strike good blows for thee."
His prayer in high Olympus heard,
Swift Mercury started at the word.
"Your axe must not be lost," said he:
"Now, will you know it when you see?
An axe I found upon the road."
With that an axe of gold he show'd.
"Is't this?" The woodman answer'd, "Nay."
An axe of silver, bright and gay,
Refused the honest woodman too.
At last the finder brought to view
An axe of iron, steel, and wood.
"That's mine," he said, in joyful mood;
"With that I'll quite contented be."
The god replied, "I give the three,
As due reward of honesty."
This luck when neighbouring choppers knew,
They lost their axes, not a few,
And sent their prayers to Jupiter
So fast, he knew not which to hear.
His wingéd son, however, sent
With gold and silver axes, went.
Each would have thought himself a fool
Not to have own'd the richest tool.
But Mercury promptly gave, instead
Of it, a blow upon the head.

    *With simple truth to be contented,*
    *Is surest not to be repented;*
*But still there are who would*    *Whose cunning is but stupid,*
*With evil trap the good,—*    *For Jove is never dupéd.*

**THE·WOODMAN·AND·MERCURY.**

# The Lion and the Monkey.

THE lion, for his kingdom's sake,
   In morals would some lessons take,
And therefore call'd, one summer's day,
The monkey, master of the arts,
An animal of brilliant parts,
   To hear what he could say.
"Great king," the monkey thus began,
"To reign upon the wisest plan
Requires a prince to set his zeal,
And passion for the public weal,
Distinctly and quite high above
A certain feeling call'd self-love,
   The parent of all vices,
   In creatures of all sizes.
To will this feeling from one's breast away,
Is not the easy labour of a day;
   By that your majesty august,
   Will execute your royal trust,
From folly free and aught unjust."
   "Give me," replied the king,
   "Example of each thing."
   "Each species," said the sage,—
   "And I begin with ours,—
Exalts its own peculiar powers
   Above sound reason's gauge.
Meanwhile, all other kinds and tribes
As fools and blockheads it describes,
   With other compliments as cheap.
But, on the other hand, the same
   Self-love inspires a beast to heap
The highest pyramid of fame
For every one that bears his name;
Because he justly deems such praise
The easiest way himself to raise.
'Tis my conclusion in the case,
   That many a talent here below
Is but cabal, or sheer grimace,—
   The art of seeming things to know—
An art in which perfection lies
More with the ignorant than wise."

THE·LION·AND·THE·MONKEY·

# The Shepherd and the Lion.

THE Fable Æsop tells is nearly this :—
    A shepherd from his flock began to miss,
And long'd to catch the stealer of, his sheep.
    Before a cavern, dark and deep,
    Where wolves retired by day to sleep,
    Which he suspected as the thieves,
    He set his trap among the leaves ;
    And, ere he left the place,
    He thus invoked celestial grace :—
    " O king of all the powers divine,
Against the rogue but grant me this delight,
That this my trap may catch him in my sight,
    And I, from twenty calves of mine,
    Will make the fattest thine."
    But while the words were on his tongue,
    Forth came a lion great and strong.
    Down crouch'd the man of sheep, and said,
    With shivering fright half dead,
" Alas ! that man should never be aware
Of what may be the meaning of his prayer !
    To catch the robber of my flocks,
    O king of gods, I pledged a calf to thee :
    If from his clutches thou wilt rescue me,
    I'll raise my offering to an ox."

THE·SHEPHERD·AND·THE·LION··

# The Horse and the Wolf.

A WOLF who, fall'n on needy days,
   In sharp look-out for means and ways,
Espied a horse turn'd out to graze.
His joy the reader may opine.
"Once got," said he, "this game were fine;
But if a sheep, 'twere sooner mine.
I can't proceed my usual way;
Some trick must now be put in play."
      This said,
He came with measured tread,
And told the horse, with learned verbs,
He knew the power of roots and herbs,—
Whatever grew about those borders,—
He soon could cure of all disorders.
If he, Sir Horse, would not conceal
   The symptoms of his case,
He, Doctor Wolf, would gratis heal;
For that to feed in such a place,
   And run about untied,
Was proof itself of some disease,
   As all the books decide.
"I have, good Doctor, if you please,"
Replied the horse, "as I presume,
Beneath my foot, an aposthume."
"My son," replied the learned leech,
"That part, as all our authors teach,
Is strikingly susceptible
Of ills which make acceptable
What you may also have from me—
The aid of skilful surgery."
The fellow, with this talk sublime,
Watch'd for a snap the fitting time.
Meanwhile, suspicious of some trick,
   The weary patient nearer draws,
And gives his doctor such a kick,
   As makes a chowder of his jaws.
Exclaim'd the Wolf, in sorry plight,
"I own those heels have served me right.
I err'd to quit my trade, as I will not in future;
Me Nature surely made for nothing but a butcher."

THE·HORSE·AND·THE·WOLF·

# The Eagle and the Owl.

THE eagle and the owl, resolved to cease
   Their war, embraced in pledge of peace.
On faith of king, on faith of owl, they swore
That they would eat each other's chicks no more.
  "But know you mine?" said Wisdom's bird.
   "Not I, indeed," the eagle cried.
   "The worse for that," the owl replied:
  "I fear your oath's a useless word;
   I fear that you, as king, will not
   Consider duly who or what:
Adieu, my young, if you should meet them!"
"Describe them, then, and I'll not eat them,"
The eagle said.  The owl replied:
"My little ones, I say with pride,
For grace of form cannot be match'd,—
The prettiest birds that e'er were hatch'd;
By this you cannot fail to know them;
'Tis needless, therefore, that I show them."
At length God gives the owl a set of heirs,
And while at early eve abroad he fares,
  In quest of birds and mice for food,
  Our eagle haply spies the brood,
  As on some craggy rock they sprawl,
  Or nestle in some ruined wall,
  (But which it matters not at all,)
  And thinks them ugly little frights,
  Grim, sad, with voice like shrieking sprites.
"These chicks," says he, "with looks almost infernal,
Can't be the darlings of our friend nocturnal.
I'll sup of them."  And so he did, not slightly:—
He never sups, if he can help it, lightly.
  The owl return'd; and, sad, he found
  Nought left but claws upon the ground.
He pray'd the gods above and gods below
To smite the brigand who had caused his woe.
Quoth one, "On you alone the blame must fall;
Thinking your like the loveliest of all
You told the eagle of your young ones graces;
  You gave the picture of their faces:—
  Had it of likeness any traces?"

## THE·EAGLE·AND·THE·OWL.

# The Miser and the Monkey.

A MAN amass'd. The thing, we know,
  Doth often to a frenzy grow.
No thought had he but of his minted gold—
Stuff void of worth when unemploy'd, I hold.
Now, that this treasure might the safer be,
  Our miser's dwelling had the sea
As guard on every side from every thief.
With pleasure, very small in my belief,
  But very great in his, he there
Upon his hoard bestow'd his care.
  No respite came of everlasting
  Recounting, calculating, casting;
For some mistake would always come
To mar and spoil the total sum.
A monkey there, of goodly size,—
And than his lord, I think, more wise,—
Some doubloons from the window threw,
And render'd thus the count untrue.
  The padlock'd room permitted
  Its owner, when he quitted,
To leave his money on the table.
  One day, bethought this monkey wise
  To make the whole a sacrifice
To Neptune on his throne unstable.
  I could not well award the prize
Between the monkey's and the miser's pleasure
  Derived from that devoted treasure.
One day, then, left alone, | That animal, to mischief prone,
Coin after coin detach'd, | A gold jacobus snatch'd,
Or Portuguese doubloon, | Or silver ducatoon,
  Or noble, of the English rose,
  And flung with all his might
  Those discs, which oft excite
The strongest wishes mortal ever knows.
Had he not heard, at last, | The turning of his master's key,
The money all had pass'd | The same short road to sea;
  And not a single coin but had been pitch'd
Into the gulf by many a wreck enrich'd.
  *Now, God preserve full many a financier*
  *Whose use of wealth may find its likeness here !*

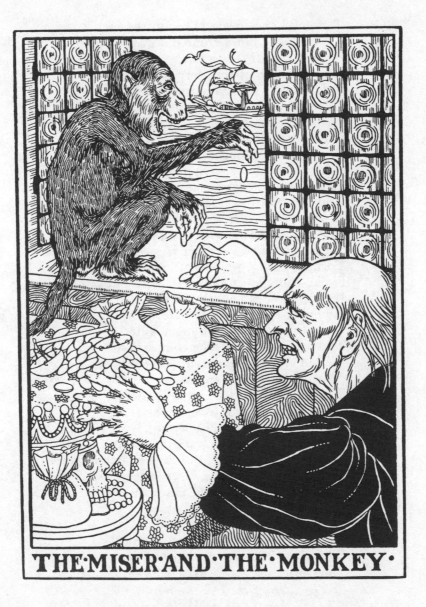

## THE·MISER·AND·THE·MONKEY·

# The Vultures and the Pigeons.

MARS once made havoc in the air:
    Some cause aroused a quarrel there
Among the birds;—not those that sing,
The courtiers of the merry Spring,
But naughty hawk and vulture folks,
Of hookéd beak and talons keen.
    The carcass of a dog, 'tis said,
    Had to this civil carnage led.
Blood rain'd upon the swarded green,
And valiant deeds were done, I ween.
Suffice to say, that chiefs were slain,
And heroes strow'd the sanguine plain.
'Twas sport to see the battle rage,
And valiant hawk with hawk engage;
'Twas pitiful to see them fall,—
Torn, bleeding, weltering, gasping, all.
Force, courage, cunning, all were plied;
Intrepid troops on either side
No effort spared to populate
The dusky realms of hungry Fate.
This woful strife awoke compassion
Within another feather'd nation,
    Of iris neck and tender heart.
They tried their hand at mediation—
    To reconcile the foes, or part.
The pigeon people duly chose
    Ambassadors, who work'd so well
    As soon the murderous rage to quell,
And stanch the source of countless woes.
A truce took place, and peace ensued.
    Alas! the people dearly paid
    Who such pacification made!
Those cursed hawks at once pursued
The harmless pigeons, slew and ate,
Till towns and fields were desolate.

*The safety of the rest requires*
*The bad should flesh each other's spears:*
    *Whoever peace with them desires*
*Had better set them by the ears.*

**THE·VULTURES·AND·THE·PIGEONS**

# The Stag and the Vine.

A STAG, by favour of a vine,
Which grew where suns most genial shine,
And form'd a thick and matted bower
Which might have turn'd a summer shower,
Was saved from ruinous assault.
The hunters thought their dogs at fault,
And call'd them off.   In danger now no more
The stag, a thankless wretch and vile,
Began to browse his benefactress o'er.
The hunters, listening the while,
The rustling heard, came back,
With all their yelping pack,
And seized him in that very place.
"This is," said he, "but justice, in my case.
Let every black ingrate
Henceforward profit by my fate."
The dogs fell to—'twere wasting breath
To pray those hunters at the death.
They left, and we will not revile 'em
A warning for profaners of asylum.

THE·STAG·AND·THE·VINE···

# The Earthen Pot and the Iron Pot.

AN iron pot proposed
  To an earthen pot a journey.
The latter was opposed,
  Expressing the concern he
Had felt about the danger
Of going out a ranger.
He thought the kitchen hearth
The safest place on earth
For one so very brittle.
" For thee, who art a kettle,
And hast a tougher skin,
There's nought to keep thee in."
" I'll be thy body-guard,"
  Replied the iron pot;
" If anything that's hard
  Should threaten thee a jot,
Between you I will go,
And save thee from the blow."
  This offer him persuaded.
  The iron pot paraded
  Himself as guard and guide
  Close at his cousin's side.
  Now, in their tripod way,
  They hobble as they may;
  And eke together bolt
  At every little jolt,—
  Which gives the crockery pain;
    But presently his comrade hits
    So hard, he dashes him to bits,
  Before he can complain.

*Take care that you associate*
*With equals only, lest your fate*
*Between these pots should find its mate.*

THE·EARTHEN·POT·AND·THE·IRON·POT.

# The Bear and the Two Companions.

TWO fellows, needing funds, and bold,
   A bearskin to a furrier sold,
Of which the bear was living still,
But which they presently would kill—
   At least they said they would,
   And vow'd their word was good.
   The bargain struck upon the skin,
   Two days at most must bring it in.
Forth went the two.   More easy found than got,
   The bear came growling at them on the trot.
Behold our dealers both confounded,
   As if by thunderbolt astounded!
Their bargain vanish'd suddenly in air;
For who could plead his interest with a bear?
   One of the friends sprung up a tree;
   The other, cold as ice could be,
     Fell on his face, feign'd death,
     And closely held his breath,—
He having somewhere heard it said
The bear ne'er preys upon the dead.
Sir Bear, sad blockhead, was deceived—
The prostrate man a corpse believed;
But, half suspecting some deceit,
He feels and snuffs from head to feet,
   And in the nostrils blows.
The body's surely dead, he thinks.
"I'll leave it," says he, "for it stinks;"
   And off into the woods he goes.
The other dealer, from his tree
Descending cautiously, to see
His comrade lying in the dirt,
   Consoling, says, "It is a wonder
   That, by the monster forced asunder,
We're, after all, more scared than hurt.
But," addeth he, "what of the creature's skin?
He held his muzzle very near;
What did he whisper in your ear?"
"He gave this caution,—'Never dare
Again to sell the skin of bear
Its owner has not ceased to wear.'"

THE·BEAR·AND·THE·TWO·COMPANIONS

# The Lion, the Wolf, and the Fox.

A LION, old, and impotent with gout,
 Would have some cure for age found out.
This king, from every species,—
Call'd to his aid the leeches.
They came, from quacks without degree
To doctors of the highest fee.
Advised, prescribed, talk'd learnedly;
 But with the rest
Came not Sir Cunning Fox, M.D.
Sir Wolf the royal couch attended,
 And his suspicions there express'd.
Forthwith his majesty, offended,
Resolved Sir Cunning Fox should come,
And sent to smoke him from his home.
He came, was duly usher'd in,
And, knowing where Sir Wolf had been,
 Said, "Sire, abused your royal ear
 Has been by rumours insincere;
To wit, that I've been self-exempt
From coming here, through sheer contempt.
But, sire, your royal health to aid,
I vow'd to make a pilgrimage,
And, on my way, met doctors sage,
In skill the wonder of the age,
 Whom carefully I did consult
 About that great debility
 Term'd in the books senility,
Of which you fear, with reason, the result.
You lack, they say, the vital heat,
By age extreme become effete.
Drawn from a living wolf, the hide
Should warm and smoking be applied.
Sir Wolf, here, won't refuse to give
His hide to cure you, as I live."
The king was pleased with this advice.
Flay'd, jointed, served up in a trice,
Sir Wolf first wrapped the monarch up,
Then furnish'd him whereon to sup.

*Beware, ye courtiers, lest ye gain,*
*By slander's arts, less power than pain.*

THE·LION·THE·WOLF·AND·THE·FOX·

# The Battle of the Rats and Weasels.

THE weasels live, no more
    than cats,
On terms of friendship with the
    rats;
  And, were it not that these
  Through doors contrive to
    squeeze
    Too narrow for their foes,
  The animals long-snouted
  Would long ago have routed,
  And from the planet scouted
    Their race, as I suppose.

One year it did betide,
When they were multiplied,
An army took the field
Of rats, with spear and shield,
Whose crowded ranks led on
A king named Ratapon.
  The weasels, too, their banner
  Unfurl'd in warlike manner.
As Fame her trumpet sounds;
  The victory balanced well;
Enrich'd were fallow grounds
  Where slaughter'd legions
    fell;
But by said trollop's tattle,
The loss of life in battle
Thinn'd most the rattish race
In almost every place;

And finally their rout
Was total, spite of stout
Artarpax and Psicarpax,
And valiant Meridarpax,
Who, cover'd o'er with dust,
Long time sustain'd their host
Down sinking on the plain.
Their efforts were in vain;
Fate ruled that final hour,
(Inexorable power!)
And so the captains fled
As well as those they led;
The princes perish'd all.
The undistinguish'd small
In certain holes found shelter;
In crowding, helter-skelter;
But the nobility
Could not go in so free,
Who proudly had assumed
Each one a helmet plumed;
We know not, truly, whether
For honour's sake the feather,
Or foes to strike with terror;
But, truly, 'twas their error.
Nor hole, nor crack, nor crevice
  Will let their head-gear in;
While meaner rats in bevies
  An easy passage win;—
So that the shafts of fate
Do chiefly hit the great.

*A feather in the cap*
*Is oft a great mishap.*
*An equipage too grand*
*Comes often to a stand*
*Within a narrow place.*
*The small, whate'er the case,*
*With ease slip through a strait,*
*Where larger folks must wait.*

THE·BATTLE·OF·THE·RATS·AND·THE·WEASELS·

# The Animals Sick of the Plague.

THE sorest ill that Heaven hath
　　Sent on this lower world in wrath,—
The plague (to call it by its name,)
　　One single day of which
　　Would Pluto's ferryman enrich,—
Waged war on beasts, both wild and tame.
They died not all, but all were sick:
No hunting now, by force or trick,
To save what might so soon expire.
No food excited their desire;
Nor wolf nor fox now watch'd to slay
The innocent and tender prey.
　　　　The turtles fled;
So love and therefore joy were dead.
The lion council held, and said:
" My friends, I do believe
This awful scourge, for which we grieve,
Is for our sins a punishment
Most righteously by Heaven sent.
Let us our guiltiest beast resign,
A sacrifice to wrath divine.
Perhaps this offering, truly small,
May gain the life and health of all.
By history we find it noted
That lives have been just so devoted.
Then let us all turn eyes within,
And ferret out the hidden sin.
Himself let no one spare nor flatter,
But make clean conscience in the matter.
For me, my appetite has play'd the glutton
　　Too much and often upon mutton.
　　What harm had e'er my victims done?
　　　　I answer, truly, None.
Perhaps, sometimes, by hunger press'd,
I've eat the shepherd with the rest.
I yield myself, if need there be;
And yet I think, in equity,
Each should confess his sins with me;
For laws of right and justice cry,
The guiltiest alone should die."
　　"Sire," said the fox, "your majesty
Is humbler than a king should be,

200

THE·ANIMALS·SICK·OF·THE·PLAGUE·

And over-squeamish in the case.
　What! eating stupid sheep a crime?
　No, never, sire, at any time.
It rather was an act of grace,
A mark of honour to their race.
And as to shepherds, one may swear,
　The fate your majesty describes,
Is recompense less full than fair
　For such usurpers o'er our tribes."

　Thus Renard glibly spoke,
And loud applause from flatterers broke.
Of neither tiger, boar, nor bear,
Did any keen inquirer dare
To ask for crimes of high degree;
　The fighters, biters, scratchers, all
From every mortal sin were free;
　The very dogs, both great and small,
Were saints, as far as dogs could be.

　The ass, confessing in his turn,
Thus spoke in tones of deep concern:—
"I happen'd through a mead to pass;
The monks, its owners, were at mass;
Keen hunger, leisure, tender grass,
　And add to these the devil too,
　All tempted me the deed to do.
I browsed the bigness of my tongue;
Since truth must out, I own it wrong."

On this, a hue and cry arose,
As if the beasts were all his foes:
A wolf, haranguing lawyer-wise,
Denounced the ass for sacrifice—
The bald-pate, scabby, ragged lout,
By whom the plague had come, no doubt.
His fault was judged a hanging crime.
　"What? eat another's grass?　O shame!
The noose of rope and death sublime,
　For that offence, were all too tame!"
　And soon poor Grizzle felt the same.

*Thus human courts acquit the strong,*
*And doom the weak, as therefore wrong.*